GLOBAL WARMING:
GLOBAL WARNING

UNITED NATIONS
ENVIRONMENT PROGRAMME

Published by the **UNEP-UK Committee**

Papers presented at the UNEP-UK Committee Briefing Conference on Global Climate Change, London

5 June 1989

Edited by

D W HALL and **J C DOORNKAMP**

Published by the UNEP-UK Committee
c/o IIED
3 Endsleigh Street
London WC1H 0DD
United Kingdom
Telephone (01) 388 2117

British Library Cataloguing in Publication Data

Hall, D. W. and Doornkamp, J. C.,
Global Warming : Global Warning
I Climate Change - science and policy reaction
II Hall, D. W. II Doornkamp, J. C.
III UNEP - UK Committee
IV Monograph

ISBN 0 9515586 0 9 Global Warming : Global Warning. (pbk)

First published 1989

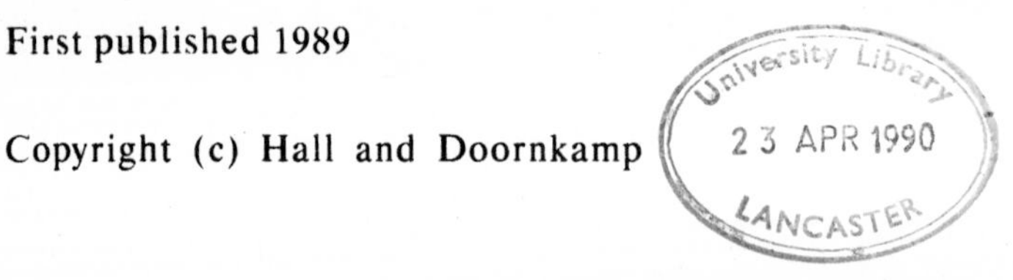

Printed in Great Britain by M1 Press, Trent Business Centre, Canal Street, Long Eaton, NG10 4HQ. (Tel: (0602) 732485).

Printed on recycled paper.

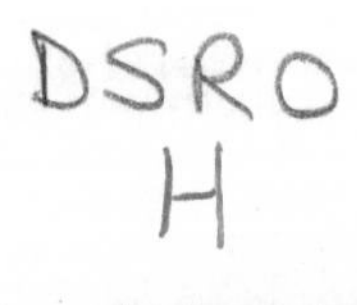

This publication is sponsored by
Rendel Environmental
A member of High-Point plc

CONTENTS

LIST OF CONTRIBUTORS

Authors of papers

Lord Caithness	Minister for the Environment
Dr H Cattle	Assistant Director, Meteorological Office
Dr P F Chester	Corporate Technical Director, National Power Division, Central Electricity Generating Board, London
Dr B W Dale	Group Leader, Chief Scientist Group, Energy Technology Support Unit, Department of Energy
Dr D J Fisk	Chief Scientist, Department of Environment
Dr K von Moltke	Conservation Foundation and World Wide Fund for Nature
J Porritt	Director, Friends of the Earth

Discussants

Dr S Boyle	Association for the Conservation of Energy
D R Cope	Director, UK Centre for Economic and Environmental Development
Dr B Denness	Director, Bureau of Applied Sciences
R Everett	Open University
M Grubb	Royal Institute for International Affairs
N Haigh	Director, Institute for European Environmental Policy
M Harper	United Nations Association
Dr A Hart	World Disarmament Campaign UK
Dr J Leggett	Director, Science, Greenpeace UK
T Roberts	World Wide Fund for Nature, UK
P Saunders	Quaker Peace and Service
E Teague	Catholic Fund for Overseas Development

FOREWORD

Dr MOSTAFA TOLBA

Executive Director,
United Nations Environment Programme (UNEP).

"The Climate Crisis" was the theme of the 1989 World Environment Day message delivered in Brussels by Dr Tolba.

The dramatic rise of the environment to summit status has been caused by the impact on the world's consciousness of two simple phrases: Global warming and ozone layer depletion.

Global warming is giving a global warning that we face climatic changes and uncertainties unprecedented in human history. We face a truly global problem. One that demands an unprecedented international response.

The economic activities of five billion human beings have replaced nature as the chief engineers of climate change. We are polluting the atmosphere with greenhouse gases - from our homes, factories, vehicles, farms, and from cutting and burning our forests.

The most vulnerable nations will be the developing countries. Geography and poverty compound their vulnerability - but the consequences will be scarcely less severe for prosperous areas of the world.

The second human assault on the atmosphere is the depletion of the ozone layer. This thin shield protects life on earth from excessive ultra-violet radiation that can cause cancer, eye damage, and injure plant and marine life - even reduce our immunity to disease.

The culprits are pollutants we send into the atmosphere - the group of gases we use in refrigeration, electronics, foams, and food packaging.

The public is already familiar with many of these problems. The question everyone is asking, is what we are doing to face the dangers, to save ourselves?

In the last two years there has been unprecedented international action. Starting late in 1987 in Montreal, nations have agreed a series of tougher measures to phase out rapidly some of these gases - and replace them with safer substitutes. UNEP has been a catalyst helping to align political action with scientific evidence.

This is not the responsibility of a few nations. It must be the common endeavour of all the world's nations. We must be ready to face the challenge of the climate crisis and the closely-linked environment crises. Challenges that are threatening our future and the future of those from whom we borrow this Earth - the generations yet to be born. This is our destiny. This is our inter-generational responsibility. The next decade is our only chance to save ourselves and to make a pact with the next generation.

Mostafa Tolba

FOREWORD

Sir PETER HARROP

Chairman,
UNEP-UK Committee

The UNEP-UK Committee was launched on World Environment Day 1988. Its purpose is to promote the work of the United Nations Environment Programme, and to stimulate action to protect and sustain the earth's environment.

On World Environment Day 1989 a Briefing Conference was held on Global Climate Change, to which we welcomed 280 participants. The subject, the greenhouse effect, is truly global, and I quote the President of the Governing Council of UNEP in May 1989, who said "a problem is pronounced global only when it is in danger of becoming apocalyptic".

The world is in fact confronted with a steady increase in greenhouse gases in the atmosphere, especially carbon dioxide, chlorofluoro-carbons and methane. These seem likely to lead to a rise in average global temperature, with daunting consequences for human society in many parts of the world. There could well be a rise in sea-levels affecting low-lying areas, as well as possible shifts in the patterns of rainfall with consequent effects on the productivity of land. More storms, more hurricanes, more floods, and more droughts can be visualised all to early.

The Briefing Conference, as shown by the contents of this volume, was intended to develop understanding of what is happening and what the results might be and, even more important to identify action to avert major calamity.

The Conference was held at the Shell Centre, the London Headquarters of Shell International Petroleum Company. We were welcomed personally by Mr Bob Reid, Chairman and Chief Executive of Shell UK, who said "it is vital for governments, industry, science and the environmental groups to get together in a spirit of co-operation, to decide priorities for the issues and agree on the best possible courses of action". The support of this Company and other parts of UK industry is gratefully acknowledged.

This publication of the Proceedings of the Conference has been financed by Rendel Environmental, to whom UNEP-UK extends its warmest thanks.

Sir Peter Harrop

PREFACE BY EDITORS

In 1972 the United Nations General Assembly established the United Nations Environment Programme and designated 5th June as World Environment Day. Governments and organisations were asked to undertake, on that day every year, activities to reaffirm concern for the enhancement of the environment.

The United Nations Environment Programme chose the theme "Global Warming: Global Warning" for World Environment Day 1989. It is appealing for more global action to contain and deal with the emerging climate change. UNEP-promoted activities have accelerated a broader awareness and understanding of the "greenhouse effect" of global warming, now known to be caused by the build-up in the atmosphere of carbon dioxide and other "greenhouse gases" discharged by industry and agriculture. If unchecked, this could alter temperatures, rainfall and sea levels beyond the ability of society to adapt. Freak weather conditions increasingly are being reported, and in the event of global warming it has been predicted that millions of people could become 'environmental refugees' in the next century.

The co-ordination of international actions to moderate climate change is one of UNEP's prime objectives.

The UNEP-UK Committee meets on or about 5th June each year to mark World Environment Day. In 1989 it arranged a Briefing Conference on 'Global Climate Change' to assess current thinking on the science, solutions and politics of the problem. The invited speakers were representative of governmental and non-governmental thinking. The participants invited were from industry, academia, media, and a wide range of non-governmental bodies.

The papers in this book record the views of speakers, offering a careful scientific review and ideas for action. They reflect the current state of knowledge. As the scientific evidence builds up there will be need for revised assessments.

Yet the threat of Global Warming is urgent and the risks, through medium term are immense. The nations of the world, in concert will shortly need to implement suitable economic and environmental policies to match the scale of the predicament facing mankind.

D W Hall J C Doornkamp

POLICY OVERVIEW

1

THE UK GOVERNMENT'S VIEW

Lord Caithness

World Environment Day, 1989, marks the fact that in a surprisingly few years the world community has grasped the issue of protecting the global environment. It now stands with prospects of success that only 20 years ago would have seemed unimaginable. However, the problems which remain are formidable, and their scale is only just being understood.

UNEP-UK's initiative in holding today's briefing and indeed its work in making UNEP better known in this country is warmly welcomed. It is also succeeding in getting British environmental achievements better known internationally. No fewer than 14 of UNEP's 1989 global 500 Awards have gone to British subjects - a remarkable tribute.

The 1989 UNEP Governing Council highlighted the very positive and practical way in which UNEP tackles global environmental issues: transfrontier movement of hazardous waste, biological diversity, depletion of the ozone layer - its whole Earthwatch Programme which offers a sound basis for international decision-making. It was a highly persuasive presentation of stark facts from Earthwatch that helped to convince people of the need for urgent action to ban the trade in new ivory, as it did for me on seeing the problem at first hand. And of course UNEP has a key role to play in securing an effective international response to global warming which the Government regards as the greatest potential threat to sustainable world development. The Prime Minister convened a seminar in early 1989 on this subject. It gave ministers a chance to listen over a full day to the views of a wide range of experts on the substance of the issues. It is hoped that colleagues in other countries will take the time to brief themselves similarly.

The belief that global climate warming represents a threat to the sustainable development of our planet is now understood by much of the community, not just the atmospheric scientists. All sectors of society have begun to take this issue very seriously, and to look at its implications. Of course there are very wide variations in estimates of the scale and the timing of man-made climate change. However, some facts are not in doubt. Many of the gases accumulate in the atmosphere with lifetimes of hundreds of years. What is more, the response of climate lags well behind the greenhouse gas concentrations. If intolerable change had to occur before action happened, then the situation would be beyond the point of no return. Furthermore, our sustainable rate of adaptation is limited; it could take half a century for a mature technology based upon coal or oil to be fully displaced from an economy by substitutes. If that seems a long time, recall that it will have taken some 20 years to replace CFCs, and they are a far less essential component of developed economies. There has not been a clearer case for the application of the precautionary principle.

Last June (1988) the message (from the Government) to the Toronto Conference on the changing atmosphere emphasised the need for further research to test the credibility of the most extreme scenarios. The Department of the Environment's research programme on climate change has increased since then, and now stands at over £0.5 million a year. The Government as a whole are spending £10 million on science related to climate change this year. It is essential spending and good value for money. The UK Meteorological Office and our scientists in the Natural Environment Research Council and universities remain amongst the world leaders in this field. However, it cannot be argued that nothing should be done until the research is watertight and comprehensive. That position could take 10 to 20 years to reach. The Government message to the Toronto Conference was that there are measures already justified in their own right which reduce the risk of climate warming, which should be taken now.

First I called for the wider ratification of the Montreal Protocol on CFCs which are long-lived and very powerful greenhouse gases, up to 20,000 times more powerful molecule for molecule than carbon dioxide. If non-ratifiers of the Protocol were to take up the production abandoned by signatories of the 1980s' growth rates, CFCs could become the dominant greenhouse gas of the next century. The Government has not just preached to the rest of the world. In March of this year, again in conjunction with UNEP, we held the London *Saving the Ozone Layer* Conference, which could not have been a greater success. A great tribute is paid to the Associated Citizens' Symposium which was so ably organised by the Green Alliance, through the good offices of the UNEP - UK National Committee. The Conference gave fresh impetus to both the Helsinki negotiations and to the whole succession of conferences that are to follow this year. The UK with other European states, has now called for the phasing-out of CFCs by the end of the century. This is in line with the call of the Toronto Conference. The United Kingdom will meet its obligation under the protocol to halve CFC consumption this year - 10 years ahead of the Treaty date.

Second, I called for a cost-effective energy efficiency policy. The Government already supports the EEC objectives of achieving a 20% improvement in the efficiency of fuel- energy demand by 1995. The UK Energy Efficiency Office (EEO) has had great success in promulgating this message. Energy efficiency, almost unknown in the 1970s, is now a key component of construction and business planning. The publicity campaigns that have brought that about may have come to the end of their useful lives, but the Government's commitment to energy efficiency in the United Kingdom most certainly has not. The EEO will now be targeting its activities more selectively, by aiming at key areas of energy use and offering specific advice backed by technical support. In particular it will:

(a) emphasise the work of regional energy efficiency officers at local level;

(b) offer a new "Best Practice" programme which will give consumers authoritative and independent advice and information on how efficient they are and how they can improve to match best practice in their sector.

The Secretary of State for Energy is also leading the campaign to increase the efficiency of energy use in the public sector. In the domestic sector the EEO will continue to devote attention to the problems of pensioners and low- income households through the Community Insulation Programme and the Homes Insulation Scheme operated by the Department of the Environment. Here, as elsewhere in the EEO's work, real economic benefit can be achieved at the same time as the environmental benefits. However, it is necessary to contain against treating energy efficiency as the cure for all ills. The public would be mislead if there were promises that energy efficiency could not deliver. As Sir Alan Cotterell wrote in *The Times* a short while ago "To conserve energy you still have to produce some energy to conserve". Whatever the role of energy efficiency in abating greenhouse gas emissions, the difficult issue of the choice of fuels nations may need to use in the future cannot be side-stepped. It is quite unhelpful and confusing to pretend, as some have done, that energy efficiency is the fifth fuel.

There is my third important option, namely proper energy pricing. Fair energy pricing incorporating full environmental costs clearly is important if a proper level of investment in energy efficiency is to be promoted and if sustainable development is to be achieved. The point may seem academic, but it is bizarre that amidst the concern over energy efficiency some nations are still heavily subsidising the consumption of energy. Also there are institutional barriers to a more rational choice of fuel. Natural gas, for example, has far less carbon per unit of energy than coal. Its greater use in the future is a major technical option. However, its use is restricted by a current EEC Directive (74/404/EEC of 13/2, 1975). The UK is leading the moves to have this directive repealed, though it appears the Commission and a number of European partners including the Dutch and Germans still have to be convinced.

Non-fossil fuel sources also have an important role to play. Sustainable use of biomass, for example, could be an important source of energy, particularly in the industrialised world. It retains the carbon in the biosphere and reduces the amount of organic material decaying to produce methane, itself an important greenhouse gas. It has its role in the industrialised world too. In the United Kingdom, some 26 schemes to use landfill gas are in operation, with 13 more in the offing. The UK potential is to save the equivalent of some 12 million tons of carbon a year. Here in the UK we must take this policy further, through other measures. Safe nuclear power is an important option for electricity generation worldwide; apart from hydro-power it is the only well established, non-carbon energy source. This was recognised by the Toronto Conference in 1988, which invited nations that have ceased nuclear programmes to review their decisions. Even with good energy efficiency a greater proportional use of nuclear power worldwide should be expected. It must not be assumed, as is reported by some, that nuclear power by itself can solve the greenhouse gas problem. There is no single option for limiting carbon emissions. The world has to pursue a package of measures, and nuclear power is an essential and an under-exploited component of that package.

The UK Government of course fully recognize the importance of having a package or diversity of fuel supplies. That is why the Electricity Bill, currently before Parliament places an obligation on public electricity suppliers to purchase a certain amount of electricity generation from non-fossil fuels. The UK it would seem is the only nation to place a commitment to a non-fossil fuel element firmly in statute.

Transport is a particularly difficult sector because here there is a more limited opportunity to use alternative fuels. It is to be regretted that this was certainly not taken into account by the European Parliament when vehicle emission standards for small cars was considered recently. There is a tendency for some countries to vie with each other to present a greener face, but at the same time to lose sight of more fundamental or long-term issues. It is to be hoped that agreement can be reached on this contentious issue in the Environment Council. It would be very good news for acid emissions, but not helpful in the reduction of carbon dioxide emissions. Engine technologies are of course available to help through the so-called lean-burn engine. The Commission is being pressed strongly to come forward with proposals that recognise the long-term implications of greenhouse gas emissions from vehicles. There is a growing recognition in Europe and the United States that vehicle fuel efficiencies must improve. More generally the unwelcome habit of the Community to pass directives without taking account of the increase in carbon dioxide generated, must cease immediately.

Finally, there is the issue of reafforestation. Present rates of forest loss, particularly in the developing world, account for some 20 % of man's carbon input to the atmosphere. Particularly worrying is the irreversible deforestation which loses once and for all the opportunity of containing some of the atmosphere's carbon in the biosphere, not to mention the loss of genetic diversity. The Overseas Development Administration (ODA) has a particularly good record in assisting developing nations with forestry. In Kenya, its current forestry initiative encourages aid partners to give greater priority to that sector. There are encouraging signs that others are seeing the wisdom of this approach. Such actions can all be taken by nations in their own interests. The scale of the problem may be such that effective action can be taken only by the world community acting in concert. There is wide international acceptance of that, as endorsed most recently (May 1989) in the UNEP Governing Council decision of which the UK was a joint sponsor.

The global environment takes no account of frontiers. Thus if Europe were heroically to cease steel production to cut down its emissions, but then import steel from elsewhere, there would be no benefit to the global environment, though there would be a severe economic cost to Europe. Failure to recognize this dimension may account for the rather arbitrary emission reductions proposed at the Toronto Conference which seem to have had little impact. International action is essential and a proper assessment needs to be made of the economics of this action.

For this reason we welcome the formation in 1988 by UNEP and the World Meteorological Organisation (WMO) of the Intergovernmental Panel on Climate Change (IPCC). The UK also co-sponsored the 1988 UN General Assembly Resolution on Climate Change, inviting IPCC to come forward with elements for a possible convention. The IPCC has an ambitious task. It also has a tight timetable, reporting to the World Climate Conference in 1990. There has never been a technical undertaking on this scale before and the UK is taking a leading part; it chairs one of the three working groups, on scientific assessment, and provides more than £0.5 million funding. We take an active part in two other working groups. The UK currently is leading work to look at the available technical options that can be deployed to abate emissions, and acting as one of the co-ordinators for inputs on possible elements of a global convention.

The Government announced a few weeks ago its own views on what shape a Convention might take; rapid progress could be made by following in the footsteps of the Vienna Convention for the Protection of the Ozone Layer.

A start could be made by setting up an umbrella, or framework Convention, laying out the general principles. The world community can then attach specific protocols to the convention as issues arise and as the science justifies.

These general ideas have already won wide approval and led directly to the decision at the May 1988 UNEP Governing Council that matters are urgent enough for UNEP to start preparatory work for a Climate

Convention, with serious negotiations to begin as soon as the IPCC has reported in 1990. The UK will play a full part in the United Nations' preparatory process.

Things may seem to be moving very rapidly, but in fact there is still a great deal to do. There have been lessons from the Montreal Protocol particularly the need to think very much more carefully about the needs of developing countries. These countries have contributed little to the global problem to date, but could face major curtailment of their economic growth if the most pessimistic scenarios are realized. Meeting their problems has been a difficult point in negotiating the abatement of CFC emissions. It will be an even more difficult task when abating other greenhouse gases. There will be a need to search vigorously for scientific, technological and economic solutions.

Nobody now doubts the UK's commitment to address this problem. The argument was laid out first at the Toronto Conference and then repeated subsequently in its response to the Brundtland Report. The Prime Minister's speech to the Royal Society in 1988 brought home to most people the threat of global climate change. Since then the UK has made a major contribution to the work of all three of the UNEP/WMO, working groups of the IPCC. It has increased the political momentum at the United Nations General Assembly and the UNEP Governing Council, and of course at the London Ozone Layer Conference. All along the UK has recognized that climate warming is a problem that can only be solved internationally and specifically through the institutions of the United Nations. Our faith in UNEP has been made clear and it is most encouraging to note the greater support that this body is receiving. There is a need to begin on the outlines of a Convention as the report of the Intergovernmental Panel (IPCC) for the 1990 World Climate Conference is awaited. So it is timely that through this World Environment Day Briefing, coming as it does at the end of the 1980s the UNEP-UK Committee should be addressing what many consider to be the greatest problem that now faces the world.

This problem presents an enormous challenge. It brings to mind the proverb: " If you are thinking one year ahead plant rice, if you are thinking ten years ahead plant trees, but if you are thinking a hundred years ahead educate the people ".

SCIENTIFIC PROBLEMS

2

THE WARMING PHENOMENON

Dr H Cattle

It is important to establish the scientific aspects of the problem of global climate change before even beginning to look for remedies. Specifically we shall here give an indication of what the greenhouse effect is; the gases that are important; how the effects of increases in the levels of greenhouse gases are estimated and how large they may eventually be; what might be expected to be seen now; the changes expected in the coming decades; and the current major unknowns in our understanding.

The greenhouse effect

The greenhouse effect itself is, of course, perfectly natural and indeed is important for sustaining life on earth. Without it surface temperatures would be some 30°C lower than they are at present. This is because the temperature of the earth's atmosphere results from an equilibrium between the radiation received from the sun and the radiation emitted by the earth. The sun's radiation, characteristic of a very hot body, tends to be of short wave-length - most obviously in the form of visible light. The radiation of the much cooler earth, on the other hand, is the relatively longer wave-length, infra-red heat radiation. The greenhouse gases in the earth's atmosphere affect the equilibrium temperature because they are largely transparent to the incoming short wave-length radiation from the sun but absorb and re-radiate some of the long wave-length radiation back to the earth, thus warming the surface. The effect is somewhat analogous to the behaviour of glass in a greenhouse and hence the common name given to these gases (Figure 1).

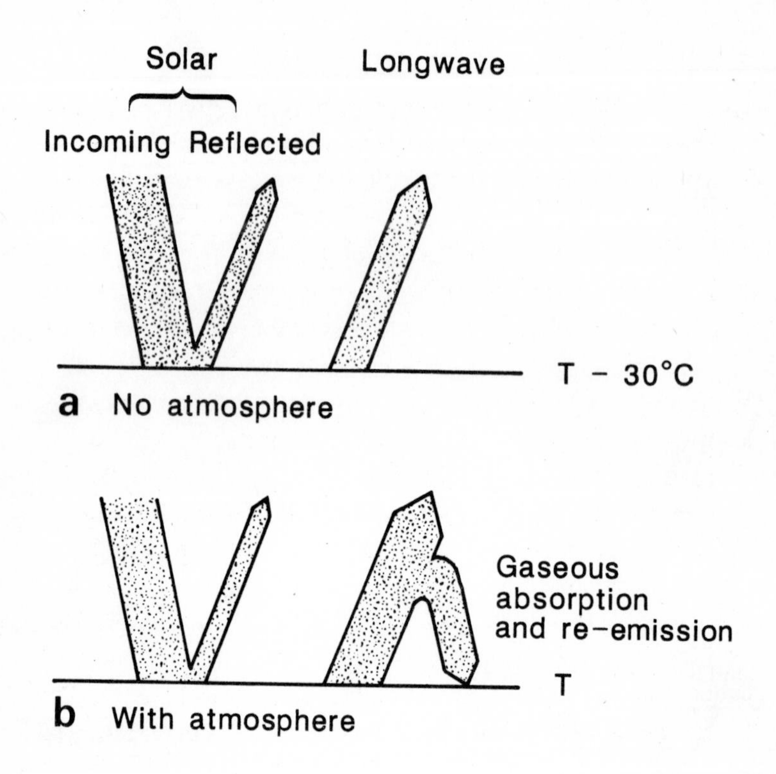

FIGURE 1 The earth is heated by solar radiation and cooled by long-wave radiation to space (top). Certain gases (mainly water vapour, also CO_2, CFCs, nitrous oxide and ozone) absorb long-wave radiation and re-radiate it back to the surface (bottom) with the result that the earth's surface is some 30°C warmer than it would be otherwise (the " greenhouse effect ").

The earth's atmosphere has always contained greenhouse gases: water vapour, which is by far the most important, carbon dioxide and methane, for example.

Current concern, however, is centred on the rapid increase in greenhouse gas concentrations due to man's activities, over and above those which are naturally present, and the likely resultant global warming which will ensue. The degree to which any particular greenhouse gas affects global warming depends on two factors: its relative effectiveness per unit concentration in blocking the radiation from the earth; and its concentration in the atmosphere. Taking both these factors into account, the principle greenhouse gases to which man contributes, in order of their potential impact on global warming, are: carbon dioxide, chlorofluorocarbons (the CFCs), methane, nitrous oxide and ozone. The combined effect of the changes in the atmospheric concentration of these gases is expected to give the equivalent of an effective doubling of carbon dioxide over its pre-industrial level of around 275 parts per million during the first half of the next century. Note that the present levels of carbon dioxide concentration are of the order of 350 ppm.

Carbon dioxide concentrations have risen over the last two decades at a rate of about 0.5 % per year. This is about half the emission rate because part is naturally absorbed, principally by the oceans. Methane levels have risen over the past decade by 1 % per year; CFCs at 5 % per year; nitrous oxide at a rate of 0.25 % per year. There is some evidence that ozone levels in the lower part of the atmosphere, the troposphere, have doubled over the last century. Note that ozone is important in a dual role: both as a greenhouse gas and in the shielding effect from ultra-violet radiation for which its concentration in the stratosphere, and in particular the development of the ozone hole, is an important issue.

The evidence for global warming may be looked for in the results of two complementary areas of work: numerical modelling and the analysis of the observed climate record.

Numerical modelling

The impact of the changes in the concentration of greenhouse gases, primarily carbon dioxide, has been investigated using models of a wide range of complexity; from very simple one-dimensional models, which attempt to represent the integrated impacts over the earth; to complex three-dimensional numerical models of the coupled ocean, atmosphere and sea ice. The simplified models have proved extremely useful for determining the radiative effects of increasing the concentration of trace gases and for analysing the strengths of the feedbacks in more complex models; they are also economical to run and relatively easy to analyse. On the other hand they cannot, of course, properly represent the range of interactive processes, many of which are geographically dependent, necessary for full quantitative appraisal of the impact of increases in trace gases. In particular, the simple models can never provide information on the regional changes in climate and regional changes are, of course, of considerable economic and social importance. Because of this, considerable effort has been directed towards developing three-dimensional general circulation models (GCMs), and in using these to estimate the patterns of climate change.

Atmospheric general circulation models are based on the equations which determine the motion of the atmosphere (wind), its thermodynamics (temperature) and conservation of water substance and mass (humidity and surface pressure). The values of the basic variables are kept at regular locations over the globe (the model grid) and at various levels in the model atmosphere. Current climate models use a grid which is typically 5 degrees of latitude by 7 degrees of longitude, with between 2 and 11 levels in the vertical. A particular and important problem is how to represent the effects of atmospheric phenomena associated with physical processes on scales smaller than that of the model grid. Such physical processes include clouds, precipitation, radiative heating and cooling and surface exchanges of heat, water and momentum. It is necessary to do this by representing ('parameterising') them in terms of the main variables on the model grid. Proper representation of such processes is of crucial importance for the modelling of climate and considerable care must be taken in their representation, (e.g. in ensuring that the numerical representations are energy conserving).

The atmosphere, oceans and cryosphere form interactively coupled components of the total climate system. It has become increasingly evident that modelling of climate change requires the atmospheric GCM to be coupled to models of the ocean that are of comparable complexity. It is also necessary to include interactive models of sea ice. As yet the representation of the oceans used in climate change models has been relatively simple. Often only the upper ocean is represented and then as a simple slab of water whose temperature responds to changes in atmospheric circulation. A number of atmospheric models have also been run coupled to dynamic ocean models going to the full depth of the ocean basins. However, the available computing power does not allow these to be run at resolutions much different from those of the atmospheric models to which they are coupled. Such ocean models are unable, for example, correctly to reproduce the strength of the main current systems or the impacts of smaller scale ocean eddies on the flow and heat transports. As yet, sea ice models used for climate change studies have represented the ice as a simple thermodynamic slab with little or no consideration of the effects of ice movement which is particularly important for the growth and decay of the Antarctic pack.

The computing power currently available allows atmospheric GCMs to run forward for periods up to decades. The resulting timeaveraged circulation averaged over, for example, all Januaries has been found to resemble the observed climatological average for January regardless of the initial conditions used. This lends credence to the broad physical realism of the model. If the CO_2 concentration in the model is then changed and the simulation is repeated, it is found that the resulting time-averaged circulation is different. Thus changes in climate due to different perturbations can be evaluated by comparing the simulations.

The problem of determining the impact of increases in greenhouse gas concentrations naturally divides into two parts: first, the study of the so-called equilibrium response and secondly, a determination of the transient response.

The *equilibrium response* is the *eventual* change in climate to a given perturbation (for example, for a specified increase in effective carbon dioxide concentration) after a period of time long enough for the climate to have settled down to an equilibrium state. The *transient* response is the *evolution* of the changes with time as the perturbation (for example, a continuous change in greenhouse gas concentrations, as observed or predicted), is applied. In the case of greenhouse warming the transient response is smaller than the equilibrium response at any given time as the large thermal inertia of the oceans slows the rate of warming.

Most effort to date in relation to investigations of global warming has gone into determining the *equilibrium response* of general circulation models to carbon dioxide increase - in particular to a doubling of carbon dioxide levels. This question has been investigated over the past few years by five different modelling centres using large-scale three-dimens-ional general circulation models. Assessment of the equilibrium response requires understanding and quantitatively realistic representation in models of the basic radiative forcing and of the relevant feedback processes. The feedback processes which have been identified as important to date are water vapour, cloud/ radiation/ temperature interactions, sea ice, snow and land ice. It is these feedback processes which lead to many of the uncertainties in determining the equilibrium changes in climate. Such atmospheric processes may amplify or reduce the effect of the gases in increasing the radiative heating of the earth. For example, in the absence of such processes, a doubling of carbon dioxide concentration would increase global mean surface temperature by some 1.2°C. Increases in water vapour, however, which would accompany the warming (due to the greater evaporation from the oceans

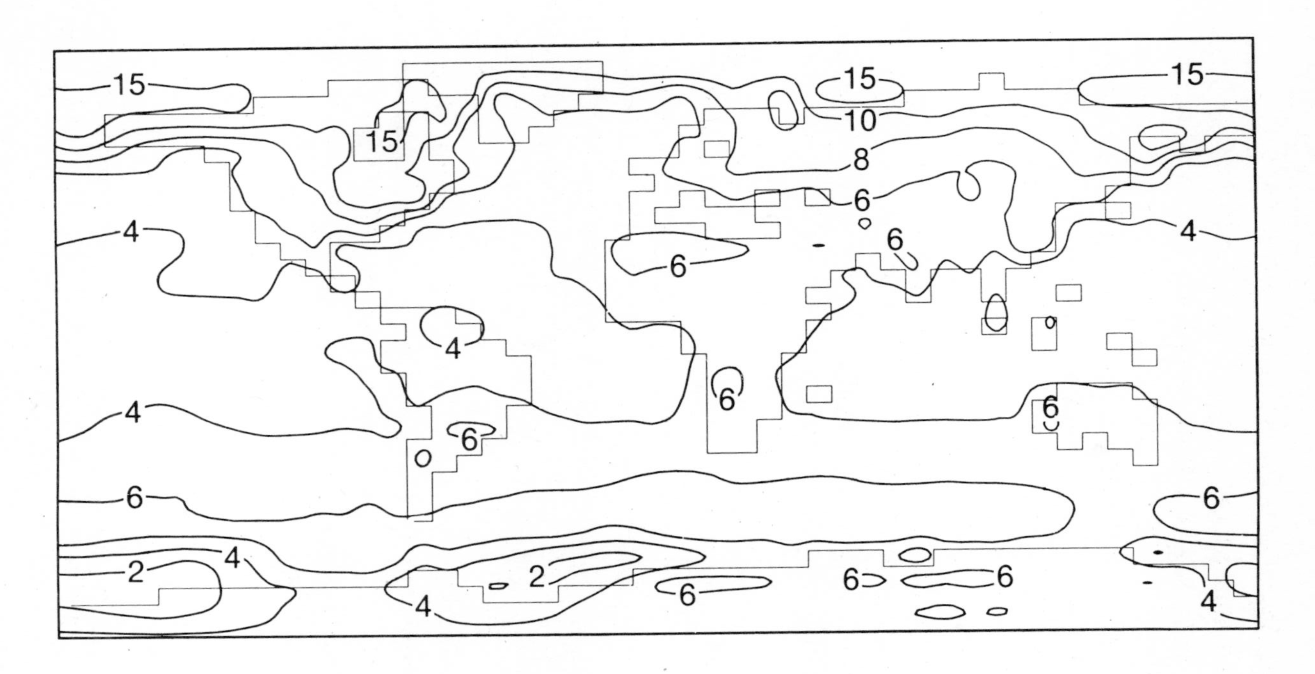

FIGURE 2 Equilibrium mean surface temperature change (°C) for December to February due to a doubling of CO_2 in a coupled atmosphere/slab ocean model.

(With permission from Wilson and Mitchell, 1987).

and the increased capacity of the atmosphere for holding the vapour), would raise the warming by about another 0.5°C. Decreases in snow and sea ice (leading to a reduction in the reflection of sunshine away from the surface) would increase this warming further by a similar amount. However, the current uncertainties in our understanding of the changes in the extent and radiative properties of cloud have led to a range of estimates in the global mean warming of between 2°C and 5°C and for this reason determination of the effect of cloudiness is currently a very important issue in climate research.

Despite such uncertainties there are a number of physical responses to the doubling of carbon dioxide which are common to all recent modelling experiments.

First, there is a warming of the troposphere and of the surface. Figure 2 shows the annual mean surface warming for a simulation at the upper end of the estimated warming range. Overall, the temperature rise increases from equator to pole. The increase in temperature resulting from the increased radiative heating of the surface by the additional CO_2 is accompanied by an increase in atmospheric water vapour content which itself further enhances the surface warming. In the tropics the warming increases with height (Figure 3), with the size of the warming varying little with season. In high latitudes, model results show, overall, that snowmelt occurs earlier and that sea ice is less extensive in the CO_2 - warm atmosphere. The largest surface warming occurs over sea ice. This is due to the change in albedo (surface reflectivity) accompanying the reduction in the extent of sea ice and the inherent low level stability of the atmosphere in high latitudes, which confines warming to the lowest levels (Figure 3). The high latitude warming is generally a minimum over sea ice in summer. The upper layers of the atmosphere (the stratosphere) show a cooling, generally of about 3°C to 4°C.

Accompanying the increase in evaporation referred to above, is a corresponding precipitation increase - globally, precipitation increases in

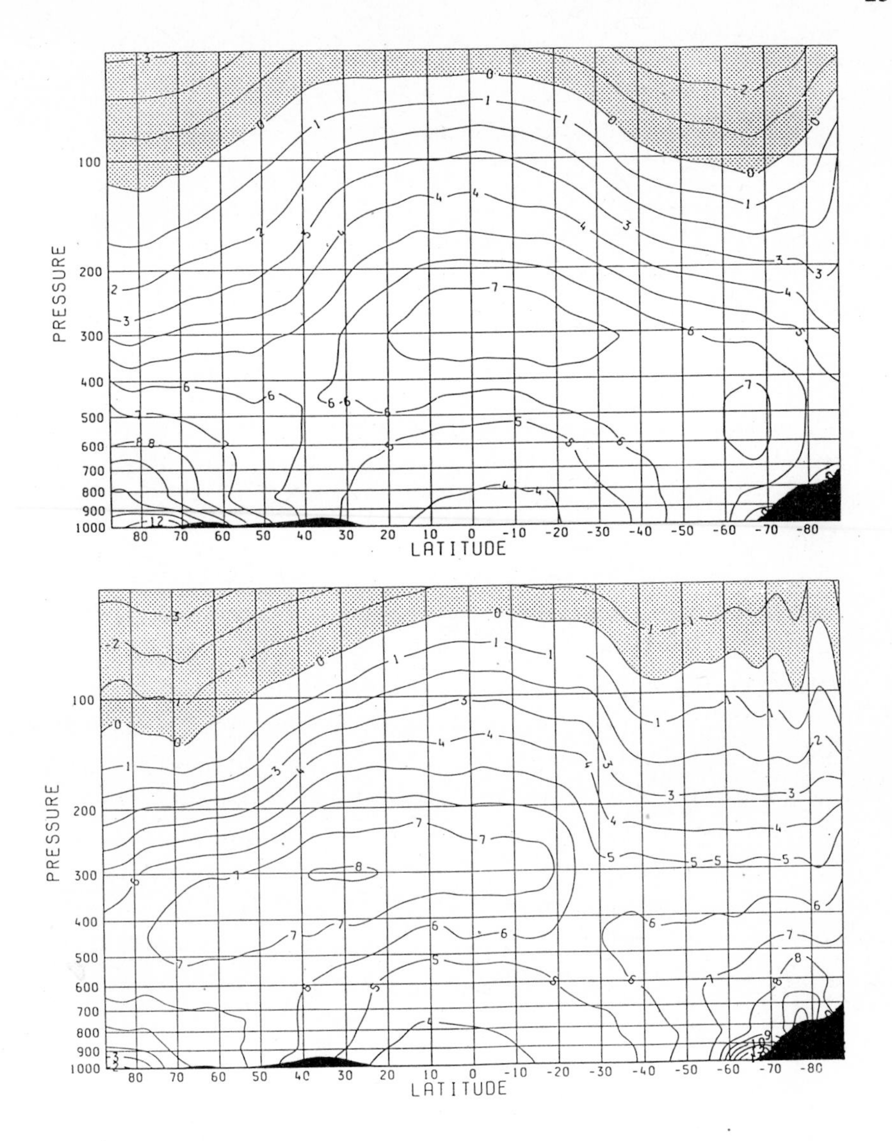

FIGURE 3 Pressure-latitude cross-sections of zonal mean equilibrium temperature change for (top) December to February and (bottom) June to August. Regions of temperature decrease are shown stipled. (With permission from Wilson and Mitchell, 1987).

all models by about 10 % on average, though, as might be expected, the geographical distribution of precipitation change is far from uniform. There is a general increase in precipitation and surface run off in high latitudes. Overall, precipitation also increases in middle and low latitudes, though locally there are regions of increase and decrease which differ from model to model. In most studies to date, there is a reduction in soil moisture over the mid-latitude continents in summer.

So far this discussion has centred around the equilibrium response of climate to an equivalent doubling of CO_2 levels. However, attention is now also being paid to the determination of the temporal response of climate to continuously increasing levels of greenhouse gas concentrations (the transient response). An important factor in slowing down the rate of warming in this context is the large capacity of the oceans to absorb the additional heating. Because of the geographical variations in the seasonal maximum mixed layer depths, and of convective processes, it is expected that the lag in ocean warming will also vary geographically. Together with the contrast between the ocean and the land, these variations may dominate the regional response to greenhouse warming over the next few decades. Detailed modelling of the oceans is therefore an essential component in determining the transient response. Other slowly responding parts of the climate system, such as sea-ice and land-ice may also require to be included.

Studies of the transient response are beginning to emerge. Recently Hansen *et al* (1988) have used a climate model (at the Goddard Institute for Space Studies) with a simplified ocean to simulate the time- dependent response to a gradual increase in trace gases. The ocean was represented in the model as a mixed layer, coupled diffusively to a deep ocean. The experiments were started at 1958 levels of trace gases and compared with the 100 year means of an experiment in which the trace gas levels remained constant. The trace gas levels were assumed to increase to give an effective doubling of carbon dioxide levels between 1958 and the year 2060. The global mean warming relative to the control constant greenhouse gas simulation was predicted to be 0.4°C in the 1990s, 1°C in the 2010s and 1.3°C in the 2020s. Changes predicted over Britain were rather similar to these.

Comparison between models and observations

Overall the global circulation models, with allowance for the damping effect of the oceans, suggest that the atmosphere should have warmed by between 0.3°C to 0.9°C over the last 150 years. The available observed global temperature records, in the case of those assembled by the Meteorological Office and the Climate Research Unit at the University of East Anglia, go back 130 years. These records show a rise of about 0.5°C since the beginning of the present century (Figure 4). However, the Meteorological Office's sea surface and marine air temperature data suggest that the latter part of the 19th century was not as cold as the early 20th century. Hence the overall warming since about 1850 may not have exceeded about 0.3°C. On the other hand the land air temperatures in the late 19th century were about 0.5°C lower than at present. The strongest warming, over both land and sea, was between about 1910 and 1940. Between 1950 and the 1970s, the northern hemisphere actually cooled, though the southern hemisphere continued to warm slightly. Both hemispheres have warmed in the last decade. The natural variations in the record mean that the predicted rise of between 0.3°C and 0.9°C is not yet statistically identifiable.

The observed warming does not, however, show the substantial enhancement predicted by models to occur in winter in high latitudes. There is also no evidence of the anticipated amplification of the warming in the tropical upper troposphere. Also, the anticipated cooling of the lower stratosphere has been evidenced only since the 1980s. However, the majority of this may have been the result of ozone depletion - the ozone hole - but a contribution of about 0.2°C to about 0.3°C from enhanced carbon dioxide cannot be discounted. In other words, the

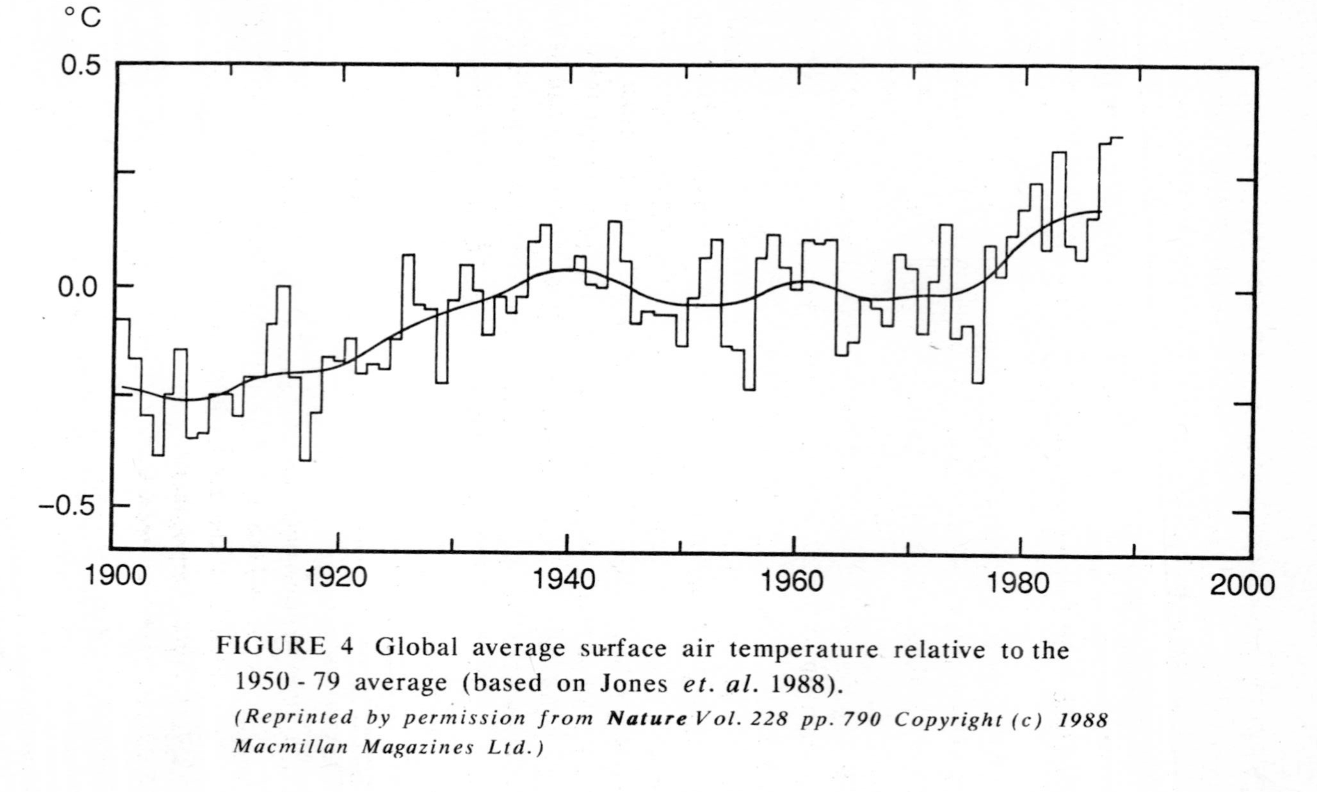

FIGURE 4 Global average surface air temperature relative to the 1950 - 79 average (based on Jones *et. al*. 1988).

*(Reprinted by permission from **Nature** Vol. 228 pp. 790 Copyright (c) 1988 Macmillan Magazines Ltd.)*

patterns of the observed changes bear only limited resemblance to the simulated equilibrium changes in models. This apparent discrepancy may arise, either from differences between the equilibrium and the transient response; they may arise due to natural variations, on the time-scale of several decades in the observed changes; or they may be due to short-comings in the representation of the relevant physical processes in the models.

Some, but not all models of the atmospheric circulation, when run with increased amounts of carbon dioxide in the model atmosphere, have indicated that the northern, mid- latitude continents (for example the mid-west of the United States) would become drier in the summer. One way in which this could manifest itself could be increased frequency of summer droughts. There have been claims, therefore, that recent climatic events such as the drought in North America are early signs of this. The drought itself was not unprecedented, however, and has been compared to the 1930s and 1950s dustbowl years, when widespread and severe droughts affected the mid-western states. As yet there seems to be no real evidence that the recent United States drought is other than a chance occurrence due to natural year to year variations and is capable of occurring without any increase in the greenhouse effect. Overall climate statistics do not seem to support the hypothesis that the observed climate extremes have yet become more frequent or severe.

Sea-level change

There is of course particular concern over the impact of global warming on sea-level rise, which for a particular warming results from a combination of thermal expansion of the oceans and the melting of continental ice-sheets and of mid-latitude glaciers. As yet general circulation models do not allow direct estimation of these effects. However, the effects of thermal expansion of the oceans may be estimated from a one-dimensional model in the absence of suitable three-dimensional experiments.

Such a model shows a rise in sea-level of 7 to 10 cm for each 1°C rise in surface temperature. The rise being the larger if the vertical mixing in the ocean is more effective. This implies that thermal expansion alone could raise sea-levels by up to 15 cm by about the year 2030.

Estimation of the effects of melting of land-ice currently relies on deductions made from running separate ice-sheet models. Recent estimates by Oerlemans (1989) show that thermal expansion, the melting of glaciers and of the Greenland and West Antarctic ice-caps are expected to contribute positively to a total change of the order of 30cm or so by the year 2030 (thought note that the likely error in these calculations is of the same order). The positive contributions of the other components are off-set to some extent by accumulation of snowfall on the remainder of the high-level Antarctic ice-cap away from the West Antarctic ice-sheet.

A global equilibrium temperature rise of 2.0°C, due to an effective doubling of greenhouse gas concentration, implies an eventual rise in sea-level of up to 1.4m resulting from thermal expansion and melting of ice. The full effect will, like the global temperature rise, be delayed due to the time taken to warm the oceans. Some have voiced fears that the Antarctic ice-cap might become unstable and slip into the sea causing sea-level rise of several metres. It is also possible, however, that increased snowfall due to higher evaporation and atmospheric moisture content could stabilize the ice-cap.

Concluding remarks

To sum up: the greenhouse effect is seen to be real and enhancing greenhouse gases will lead to a warming. However, the size of the eventual global warming resulting from a given increase in gases is uncertain (by a factor of two or more) largely due to uncertainties in modelling cloud. There is even greater uncertainty in the regional patterns of the warming.

It is important, in interpreting the results of predictions of greenhouse gas induced warming, to distinguish between those for the equilibrium warming for a given increase in greenhouse gas concentration (a doubling of CO_2, for example), and the warming at any given time in the situation where (as is actually happening) the levels of greenhouse gases are continually increasing. In the latter case, even when the effective levels of CO_2 have actually doubled, the warming by that time can be expected to be less than the equilibrium warming which would eventually be reached if the levels of greenhouse gas concentration then remained constant. This is due to the thermal inertia of the oceans which slows up the rate of warming. No model as yet incorporates a detailed dynamic description of ocean circulation, though such developments are in hand.

As it is, on the basis of the present increase in greenhouse gas concentrations over and above pre-industrial levels, a global mean rise in temperature todate of between 0.3°C to 0.9°C, is expected to have been observed. In itself this is not inconsistent with the observed rise between 0.3°C to 0.6°C. With the increase in greenhouse gas concentrations envisaged over the next 50 years or so an additional warming of between 0.5°C to 1.5°C over and above that already estimated for the present day would be expected. In both cases, due to the slowing of the rates of warming by the oceans, there is an additional long-term warming commitment amounting to an additional 1.2°C to 3.5°C for likely levels of greenhouse gas concentrations in the 2030s. There are corresponding transient and long-term commitments to sea-level rise, which may be by some 30cm by about 2030.

Numerical models of climate indicate that variables other than temperature, notably rainfall, will be affected and that changes will vary with region and season. As yet the size and location of the changes is uncertain. Although the global average temperature change observed over the present century is consistent with the mid to lower range estimates of numerical models, nevertheless, the observed regional changes in temperature are in many places inconsistent in the model predictions.

Finally, there is no compelling evidence as yet that climate has become more variable or extreme, though that does not discount greater levels of climatic variability for the future.

REFERENCES

HANSEN, J., FUNG, I., LACIS, A., RIND, D., LEBEDEFF, S., RUEDY, R. & RUSSELL, G., 1988. Global climate changes as forecast by Goddard Institute for Space Studies three-dimensional model. *J. Geophys. Res.* 93, D8, 9341-9364.

JONES, P.D., WIGLEY, T.M.I., FOLLAND, C.K., PARKER, D.E., ANGELL, J.K., LEBEDEF, S. & HANSEN, J.E., 1988. Evidence for global warming in the past decade. *Nature,* 228, 790.

OERLEMANS, J., 1989. A projection of future sea level. Submitted to *Climatic Change.*

WILSON, C.A. & MITCHELL, J.F.B., 1987. A doubled CO_2 sensitivity experiment with a GCM including a simple ocean. *J. Geophys. Res.* 92, 1315-1343.

3

GREENHOUSE GAS HEADROOM

Dr D Fisk

The previous chapter has identified many of the uncertainties in climate forecasting. However, it must be confessed that even if an accurate climate forecast for the year 2050 was available, it would be very difficult to identify the implications for the world economy or even for the regional economy of Europe or indeed the local economy of the United Kingdom.

In order to untangle such uncertainties, it is important first of all to establish what we do know. Secondly it is necessary to show how tolerable limits to possible climate change might be identified. Next there is a need to show how setting such limits simplifies the attack on the problem, using the example of identifying priorities for different greenhouse gases. Finally it has to be shown how the approach adopted permits some insights into the economics of the issue.

First, what is known? The measured concentrations of certain gases in the atmosphere have been rising over the last 100 years and are likely to continue to rise, but at rates which are rapid compared with historic time-scales. Whilst some of these changes may in part be the result of non-anthropogenic changes in the biosphere, at least one group of these gases, the CFCs is entirely man-made in origin. For the others, there is convincing circumstantial evidence to suggest that a major part of the increase is associated with man's activities.

Secondly, unless there is a most fundamental error in the understanding of basic science, it is known that the rise in concentration of these gases must be changing the radiative heat balance of the earth. In fact the radiative effect of these gases can be demonstrated in any school laboratory. Unfortunately, the scale of the problem is not dominated by the gases themselves, but by the feedback effects they induce in the climate system. Typical estimates suggest feedback effects perhaps a factor of three larger than the direct radiative effect of the key greenhouse gases.

There is a way of looking at this problem without simply getting into the 'more research is necessary' mode of thinking. More research is certainly necessary, but to wait presents special hazards. Many of these greenhouses gases have lifetimes in the atmosphere of over 100 years, and responses to reduce the emissions of the most economically useful could take half a century. It follows that it is necessary to be cautious of any proposition that encourages a 'wait and see' policy. How then to proceed? In the following, it is suggested that matters are greatly improved if the international community addresses one particular issue *i.e.* what range of climate change does it think is tolerable. This argument parallels in many ways that of determining a river quality objective well before there is concern about river pollution. By adopting this approach it is then possible to establish priorities in attending to greenhouse gases.

What might the broad criteria look like. One possible climate criterion, proposed by a Germany study, was that for the Earth to take more than a 1°C-2°C rise above present levels could be unwise at present levels of knowledge. The validity of that conclusion need not be pursued but one can imagine the factors that would have to be considered, such as sea level rise, or ecosystem stress. Indeed, the Department of the Environment's own desk studies (provided under contract to the Natural Environment Research Council) have certainly shown that for the UK, temperature rises of that order would undoubtedly be discernible. Of course for other parts of the world the critical climate criteria might be framed in terms of rainfall changes rather than temperature.

A rise in excess of 2°C would mean a move into a world in which climate models cannot necessarily be trusted or validated, and this limit too could provide a form of climate quality criterion. Finally, there may come a point at which the response of the biosphere itself becomes an important part of the uncertainty. For example, as the oceans warm up, their ability to absorb carbon dioxide in solution actually reduces. At the moment it is estimated that about half of the carbon dioxide which is emitted from the earth ends up in the oceans. This figure would change for a warm ocean, or an ocean with a great deal of absorbed carbon dioxide, or one induced to circulate in a different fashion. This would imply that for some upper limit the ability of the oceans to take some of the emissions would decline and atmospheric accumulation of greenhouse gases would increase. It has also been pointed out that as the permafrost warms there may be a release of carbon into the atmosphere as that particular ecosystem changes. Avoiding these additional positive feedbacks might suggest another limit for climate change criteria, at least as seen from the present standpoint.

Another type of climate criterion that has been proposed is based on the rate of adaptation that people can tolerate. As Dr Cattle showed (Chapter 2) at the beginning of the century global average temperatures were rising quite rapidly for a short period. That rise appeared to have been tolerated without great concern, so it might provide a comfortable limit for the acceptable rate of change. For the world economies the factors determining this acceptable rate of change involve social factors, relocation of populations, changes in economic structure and agricultural practice. For natural ecosystems the tolerable rate of adaptation is determined by the ability of ecosystems to shift and migrate to locations in which the climate is becoming more suitable. All these factors suggest possible maximum rates of change of global average temperature beyond which we would not wish to commit ourselves. Therefore although there is much work to be done, it may be possible to identify in rough terms the kind of climate change which might be tolerated. If that can be done it is possible to approach separately the distinct issue of estimating with models just how far the current situation is from breaching the established limit.

To illustrate how the next step would proceed, it is necessary to consider only one of these climatic criteria; that of an upper temperature rise limit has been chosen for this discussion. A similar argument of course could be worked through for an upper rate of rise of temperature. It is not necessary to look in detail at the effects which would encourage the setting of that limit but rather to consider the way in which identification of such a limit may help in the handling of possible uncertainties.

Climate Change Headroom

Following the arguments presented in Chapter 2, an upper temperature rise limit effectively leads to an estimate of an upper concentration limit of greenhouse gases. At the moment the world is very gradually filling up the headroom between the present concentration level and the concentration limit implied by the hypothetical climate criterion chosen for discussion. If this concept is inverted a rather familiar paradigm is obvious, not far from the paradigm used at the time of the 1970s oil crises. At that time it was concerned about using up the world's reserves of oil. Today apparently it is using up a different reserve, the capacity of the atmosphere to absorb greenhouse gases without breaching the tolerable climate change limit. Thinking about the greenhouse gases is really then a process of thinking about how exhaustion of that climate change headroom will be managed.

Different Gases Different Lifetimes

To illustrate the use of this idea of 'headroom' (without getting involved in too much detail), it is possible to look at the example of selecting a policy for different gases. As recent public debate on car emissions has shown, it is by no means easy to determine the relative importance of different gases such as carbon dioxide and ozone. Even if one is talking about a 2°C rise, that is quite a long way from breaching a tolerable limit, indeed at least a half a century on some of the projections. On the other hand, at least some of the most powerful greenhouse gases which have been mentioned already have a lifetime which extend well over that period. It follows that the first priority is to avoid filling up the available headroom of greenhouse gas concentrations, by reducing emissions of the most powerful and most long-lived of the greenhouse gases. Indeed, the CFCs have become a high priority for phasing out by the end of this century. Turning from CFCs, the concept of the headroom leads to looking next at another weaker greenhouse gas, carbon dioxide. Carbon dioxide emissions from fossil fuel sources introduce carbon into the biosphere which may not be removed for several centuries, and of which about half is partitioned in the atmosphere. These two gases have naturally figured strongly in recent debate.

Later in the order of priority there are the short-lived gases such as ozone or methane. These are powerful greenhouse gases, but with lifetimes short compared with time to exhaust the greenhouse gas headroom. The lifetime of ozone is very short and therefore once action is taken to reduce its generation, concentrations fall rapidly.

Methane provides a good example of how priorities change as the headroom is exhausted. It is a powerful greenhouse gas, about thirty times more powerful, molecule for molecule, than carbon dioxide. It is reactive so it does not last very long in the atmosphere - its lifetime is usually quoted in the order of a decade after which it returns to the biosphere as carbon, and joins the same carbon cycle as the weaker carbon dioxide emissions. It follows that methane from natural gas as an energy source is certainly a currently preferred option because its energy content is higher per unit of carbon it contains and therefore it is a rather low CO_2 emitter with respect to the amount of useful energy delivered. Indeed for this reason the United Kingdom has pressed strongly for the role of natural gas in electricity generation to be reappraised in the European Community. However, as in the future the headroom on greenhouse gases is approached it would be necessary to look again at methane because methane leaked from distribution systems, or through imperfect combustion, may still be around at the time the limit can be expected to be breached. The enhanced greenhouse effect of methane, some 30 times that of carbon dioxide, would then change the priority given to methane as a fuel. This example shows that the headroom changes the timing priorities between different gases. CFCs are a very important priority now, a long way from breaching the greenhouse gas limit, but methane and ozone represent priorities much further into the future.

The same argument can be applied to the role of methane in landfill gas which is an important option because it displaces the burning of fossil fuels elsewhere in the economy. Otherwise it is doing no more than intercepting carbon in the form of landfill gas which would have leaked into the atmosphere anyway. According to this argument, the economy is getting extra value for money in terms of burning or recovery of the landfill gas. It is not surprising that biomass is an important option in many of the long-term projections for low CO_2 emissions. However, as the top of the headroom is approached, burning landfill gas becomes an even more attractive option because now it becomes very important to convert escaping methane directly to carbon dioxide to reduce the overall greenhouse gas effect of methane. Again the model indicates that the priority for landfill gas combustion changes with time. At the moment landfill gas combustion is displacing fossil fuels, but at some later date it becomes part of a strategy to reduce the amount of methane in the atmosphere.

Carbon headroom as a resource

At the time of the energy crisis, there was much debate as to how energy prices, rising with time, would eke out energy supplies. If greenhouse gas headroom could be sold, then the same argument might apply. However, matters are hardly that straightforward, and although there has been talk of carbon taxes their complexity lies outside the scope of this commentary. Taxes on greenhouse gases may be an appropriate administrative solution to reduce emissions, but whatever method is applied to meet the headroom constraint its effect is the same. As emissions are abated the least valued uses need to be abandoned first. In effect the 'cost' of being allowed to use up part of the headroom is rising with time.

This argument also gives an insight into the old chestnut of nuclear versus energy conservation, to which the Minister has referred (Chapter 1). During the energy crisis it is doubtful whether anyone supposed that either of those two options solved the problem as it were single-handed. Similar logic ought to apply here as the limit of carbon headroom is approached. Fossil fuels emissions would represent a declining proportion of total emissions, and more expensive non-greenhouse gas fuels would come on stream. More expensive fuels induce more energy conservation, and greater energy efficiency in turn reduces the amount of the more expensive fuel that is required. Naturally an economic balance has to be struck between these two approaches. They are not alternatives.

Conclusions

These examples ought to show how the concept of a greenhouse gas headroom indicates timings and priorities. How does it influence the issue of what should be done now? Again the analogy with the energy crisis holds good. There was great uncertainty in the 1970s as to the reserves of fossil fuel available. Climate models play a very similar role. In ten to twenty years understanding of the available headroom will be much better, as indeed will be knowledge from geological investigation of how much fossil fuel there is available. In either case, having recognised first the tolerable limit, it is necessary to agree design margins that reflect the uncertainty in the modelling, and the intention of using a precautionary principle. It is also clear that the relative importance of different greenhouse gases will be affected by the type of limit the international community settles upon. It follows that the headroom needs to be managed, as it were, through international understanding and international agreements. But if that is going to happen, then surely there must be a consensus, not only on the projections of future climate change, but also their effects on natural and social systems. That is one of the important parts of the Department of the Environment's programme and our work on the Intergovernmental Panel on Climate Change.

Ten years ago people would have simply said that these sort of agreements were just not possible, but the Montreal Protocol has dispelled that possibility. It appears possible for the international community, working closely with science, to come to conclusions on the targets and dates that they wish to reach. The Minister saw this as a very difficult and challenging task, but I think this science, unlike some other research issues, is one that has a timescale of solubility. There is thus a real opportunity for the international community to begin to develop the criteria by which it wishes to time and pace its approach to managing the greenhouse gas headroom.

PRACTICAL APPROACHES

4

PRIORITIES

Dr B W Dale

Solutions to "the problem" implies that there is a problem and that there is a solution. Such a notion in the case of global warming ought to be dispelled because there is not so much a problem as a very large uncertainty. What is required is a cheap insurance policy against that uncertainty resolving itself in an unfortunate way.

An appropriate programme of response to such uncertainty might be to:

- investigate the science
- pursue cost-effective abatement
- research radical measures

Much scientific effort needs to be expended in order to understand the problem. Scientists need to answer questions such as: is the human contribution to the greenhouse effect real? When is it likely to impinge? In which way is it going to impinge? Is it about climate change, rising sea-levels, or both?

Until such time as the scientific issues are resolved prudence would indicate a programme of cost-effective abatement measures. Implementing such measures can only be a good thing, for they have two important attributes; if, in the end, the greenhouse effect is something which need not be a cause for worry, but in the meantime cost-effective abatement measures are taken up, then economies will have benefited, and nothing will have been lost. However, if the greenhouse effect turns out to be real, and abatement is necessary, then the introduction of measures capable of achieving cheap abatement at an early date will have been worthwhile.

The third need, for research into 'radical measures' seems appropriate even if the taking of them is seen by some as premature, for doing so would avoid a damaging time-lag should they be needed for immediate implementation in an emergency.

Emphasis will be given in this Chapter to UK economics and what might be done in the UK to ameliorate greenhouse gases, especially carbon dioxide the most important gas and one about which enough is known to allow the problem to be tackled. It is actually quite difficult to see how to tackle some of the other gases; in the case of CFCs, action is being taken already but they have of course a very long residence time in the atmosphere.

A breakdown of where carbon dioxide comes from, as far as the UK economy is concerned is shown in Table 1. The main source is the burning of coal, with significant contributions from the burning of oil and gas; there is a small contribution from the burning of waste.

TABLE 1

CURRENT LEVEL OF EMISSIONS

	CO_2 M. TONNES	% OF TOTAL
Coal	260	44
Oil	205	35
Gas	110	19
Waste	11	2
	-----	-----
TOTALS	586	100

An analysis of coal burning (Table 2) shows that roughly one-third of the emission comes from power stations in the generation of electricity, with small contributions from industry and the domestic sector.

TABLE 2

EMISSIONS FROM COAL BURNING

	CO_2 M. TONNES	% OF TOTAL
Electricity generation	183	31
Industry	53	9
Domestic and service	22	4
	----	----
TOTALS	258	44

Similarly, a break down for oil (Table 3) shows that roughly 20 % of the total emissions come from oil used in transport, with smaller contributions from other sources.

TABLE 3

EMISSIONS FROM THE USE OF OIL

	CO_2 M. TONNES	% OF TOTAL
Transport	125	21
Heat	57	10
Domestic and service heat	22	4
	----	----
	204	35

This breakdown implies that there is not likely to be any single magic solution to the problem. It is going to be a matter of taking a bit off here and a bit off there to reduce the problem overall. In order to achieve this a number of measures have to be considered. The order in which they actually might start to make an impression - not in order of their size, nor the order in which they might be implemented, but the order in which they might start to make a difference is:

- Waste Burning
- Energy Efficiency
- Fuel Switching
- Nuclear Power
- Renewables
- Decarbonisation
- Transport Fuels
- Reafforestation

growth. The line labelled 'might be required' represents the path which it might be necessary to achieve. If the climatologists said it was essential to follow this line in Figure 5 could the UK achieve that goal? That is, from the position of the 'no action' line in Figure 5 can the gap labelled 'Δ' be bridged?

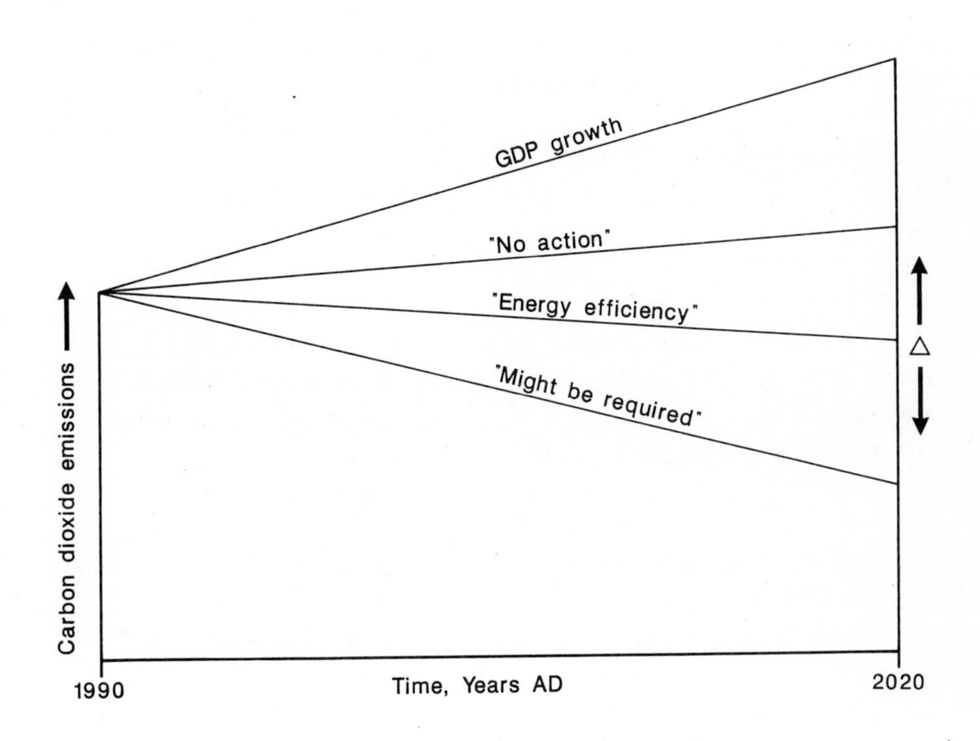

FIGURE 5

Possible future changes in CO_2 emission levels in the UK.

In order to answer this question it is first necessary to consider the measures required to achieve the difference between GDP growth and energy growth in the economy. It means achieving growth in the economy with less unit energy or using less energy per unit of production than before. How are such improved energy efficiency achieved? There are a number of reasons why energy efficiency improves in the economy on a more or less automatic basis, as a result of market forces. First power generation technology continues to improve and power stations become steadily more efficient. Second, greater efficiency in utilisation occurs (e.g. as old houses are knocked down and new ones with better insulation are built, or as people purchase more energy efficient cars). Finally there is restructuring within the economy as seen over recent years as the economy moves away from energy intensive industries into less energy intensive industries. This tendency is likely to continue.

The upper triangle between GDP Growth and 'no action' (in Figure 5) is what might be called the 'successful energy efficiency market', a market driven entirely by market forces; people investing in technologies that are more energy efficient than previously. If this market is compared with that between the 'no action' line and the 'energy efficiency' line, (or the 'energy efficient unsuccessful market' which is not active when left purely to market forces) it can be seen that the former market is actually larger than the latter one. Thus the additional energy efficiency programme does not involve a very major change because it is improving the energy efficiency performance by only perhaps 50 %, to produce a market which is 50 % larger than the already successful market. Analysis carried out at ETSU, and elsewhere, indicates that the measures that lie inside that market, would be cost-effective: that is achieve an acceptable return on investment. If measures that exist and which are cost-effective are taken up, the achievement is calculated to be 40 % of the difference between the 'no action' line and the line 'might be required' in Figure 5, 40 % of the designated 'Δ' would have been achieved.

The reasons the lower energy efficiency market is not as active as it might be have been analysed many times and the principal cause is the lack of targeted and reliable information. This situation could be improved, and it is current Government policy to help to achieve this.

It is now necessary to consider how (Figure 5) it is possible to get from the 'energy-efficiency' line to the 'might be required' line . There are essentially two ways of doing the analysis. First it is possible to say that each measure will achieve a certain fraction of the total abasement required, giving numbers which are totally defensible and easy to understand; how much nuclear power could contribute, how much fossil fuel switching could contribute, how much renewables could contribute, and so on. Although one may argue with the numbers, they would have been derived from some very firm base. They would, however, contain a lot of double counting, because if a ton of carbon dioxide is saved by energy efficiency it would not be there to be saved by fossil fuel switching. So even though these numbers are defensible and very simple, they do present a difficulty in the sense that they don't actually indicate whether it would be possible to achieve ' Δ ' or not.

Another possibility is simply to say that 40 % of the target can be reached by energy efficiency, leaving 60 %. A certain amount of this then might be nibbled off, first by say fossil- fuel switching; and so on through the list of options. This requires a very complete analysis, since you have to know how the energy efficiency achievements were made e.g. by reducing electricity consumption, or coal consumption or whatever. Unless the 'content' of the energy efficiency market has been analysed it is not possible to achieve what has been suggested . However, assumptions can be made. This would give a set of numbers which might be very approximate but there would be no double counting. By this means it would be possible to indicate whether it would be possible to reduce carbon dioxide emissions by roughly 50 %.

The assumption made here is that past trends in the pattern of energy efficiency improvement continue into the future. The assumed trends are based on the results of a number of studies of how energy efficiency improvements evolved in the past. It is then possible to work out roughly what the demand pattern will be after the energy efficiency improvements have taken place and simply to allocate market shares for the demand part of the market: some to coal, some to gas, some to electricity and so on. It is also assumed that 40 % of the electricity market is available to nuclear power, 20 % is available to renewables and 40 % is available to fossil fuels (N.B. these are approximate percentages derived from other analyses).

This approach would give the numbers shown in (Table 4). If all waste in the UK were to be burnt, there would be roughly a 2 % contribution to the 'Δ' gap (Figure 5). But also there would be a double benefit (Table 4) because of the destruction of methane.

Utilisation technologies make a 40 % contribution to 'Δ'. Switching from coal burning to gas burning, and going to combined cycle in electricity generation will make, (on the assumptions outlined earlier) a 12 % contribution to the total. Nuclear power makes an 11 % contribution and renewables 7 %. All the figures given up to this point in Table 4 are free of double counting.

Decarbonisation is slightly different. There is some possibility that in the future it will not be seen as an expensive technology although it cannot be said to be cost-effective; it has been included by way of illustration and to put a marker down, because perhaps by the year 2020 (the time horizon used here) there might be in the UK a demonstration plant in which decarbonisation is being achieved and which might be making a small contribution, (possibly 2 %).

With new transport fuels compressed natural gas is assumed to have penetrated about half way into the transport market to provide an additional contribution of 5 % by the year 2020.

Finally for the UK, if the land given over to forestry were to be doubled that would make a contribution of approximately 2 %.

Addition of all of the above contributions comes to about 80 %. Thus if the climatologists stated that the UK had to reduce its carbon dioxide emissions by 50 %, then by deploying the cost-effective measures considered above it might be possible to get to 80 % of that objective.

TABLE 4

DEMAND PATTERNS FOLLOWING ENERGY EFFICIENCY IMPROVEMENTS

	% Contribution to 'Δ '
Waste burning	2 + +
Energy efficiency	40
Fuel switching	12
Nuclear power	11
Renewables	7
Decarbonisation	2
Transport fuels	5
Reforestation	2

In essence therefore a 50 % reduction is not a totally unfeasible target, although it would be very difficult to achieve. The tentative conclusion would be therefore that cost-effective measures alone could not achieve a 50 % reduction in CO_2 emissions in the UK over 30 years. Achieving such a target would require additional expenditure.

5

IMPLICATIONS FOR INDUSTRY

Dr P F Chester

The reference point of a 50 % cut by about the year 2020, set out in Chapter 4, is important and means a 2.3 % reduction per year. Putting that in context, it is worth considering how the CO_2 concentration in the atmosphere would build up for different rates of rise of emissions.

If emissions of CO_2 rose at 2.5 % a year, the doubling that most people feel would have serious climatic consequences would be reached in something like 40 years (Figure 6). If CO_2 emissions are kept constant, a doubling in concentration would require nearly 150 years. Thus the first commentary is that the present global growth rate certainly must be reduced. Whatever the problem, it will be on us very quickly if emissions are allowed to grow at that rate.

Secondly, getting to zero growth will be difficult enough and getting below zero may be too ambitious a target for the moment. The Toronto Conference target is approximately a 1.3 % reduction per year while a 50 % cut in 30 years is about a 2.3 % reduction per year. These perhaps, are eventual targets to be adopted. But even getting to a world cap would be extremely beneficial and getting away from a 2.5 % increase per year seems absolutely essential.

Who is using the energy is important and is indicated in Figure 7 which shows clearly that there is a vast difference between the less developed countries (LDCs), the Centrally Planned Economies (CPEs) and the United States, Japan and Western Europe. Also it shows the improvements which have taken place in the last 10 years in the USA where

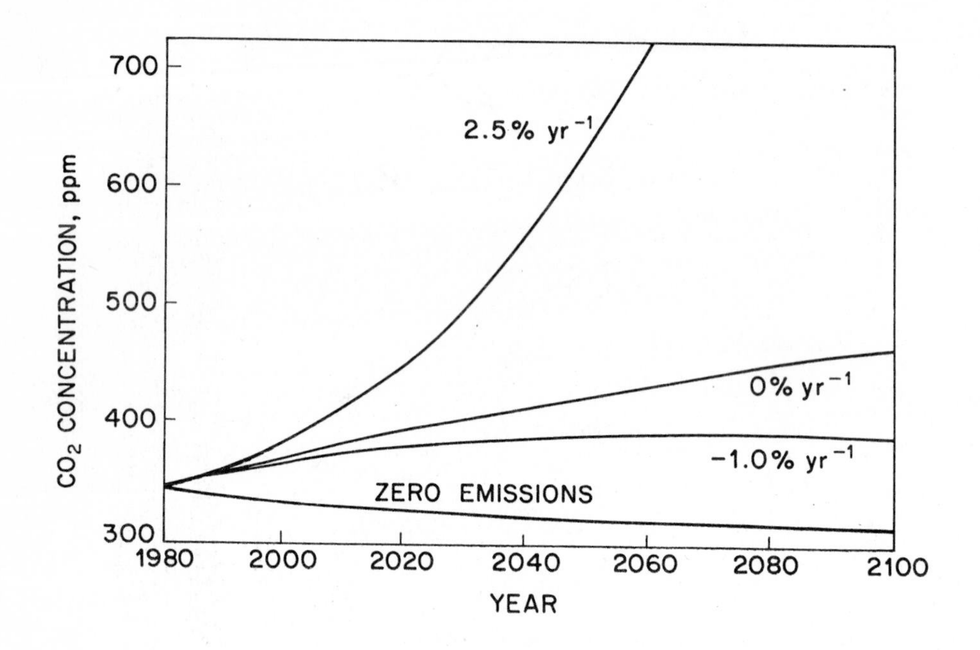

FIGURE 6

Projected atmospheric CO_2 concentrations for a range of future CO_2 - input scenarios.

consumption has been pulled back to about their 1967 level.

How energy consumption relates to growth in GDP (Gross Domestic Product) is shown in Figure 8, indicating how things have been improving for some time in the United States, Western Europe and

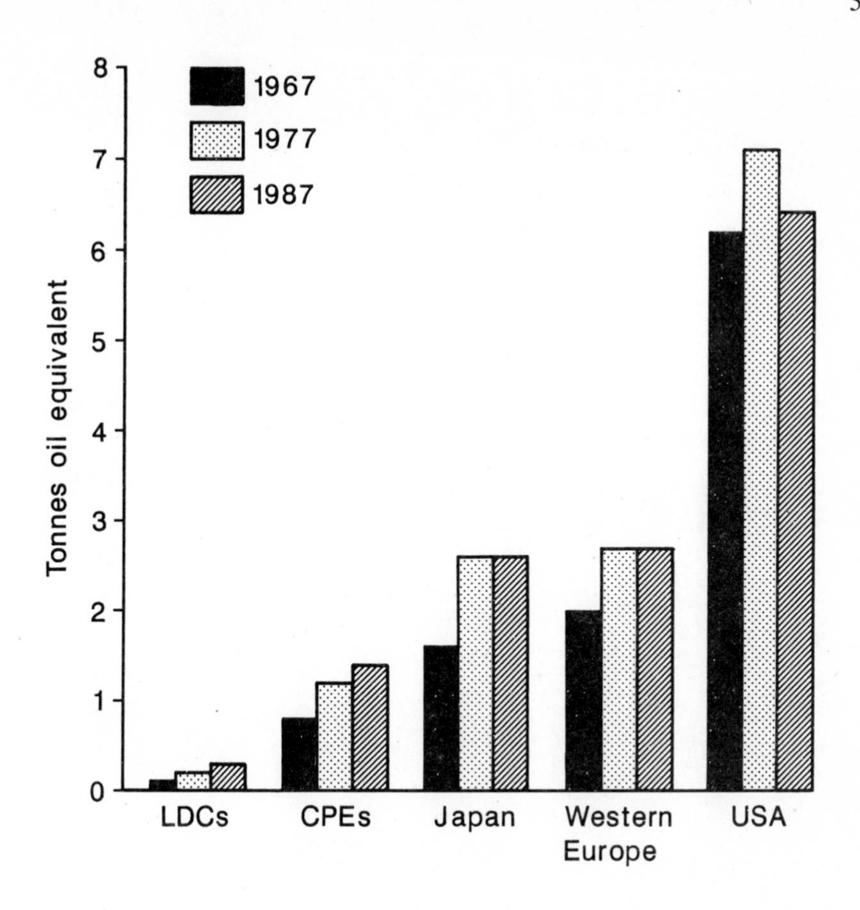

FIGURE 7

Global variations in the use of energy.

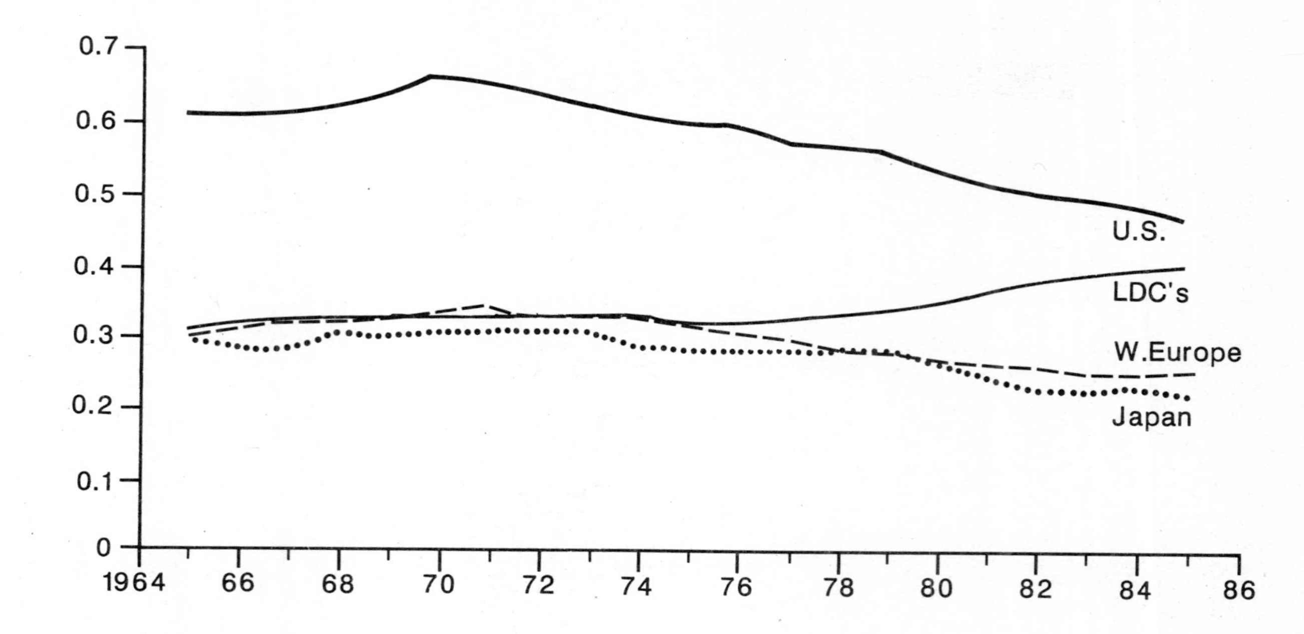

FIGURE 8 Energy consumption / GDP

Japan. There is of course still a lot of room for further improvement in these countries. In the less developed countries, for understandable reasons, energy consumed per unit of GDP is going up, largely because of population expansion. Indeed the GDP per capita in the poorest of the less developed countries is actually declining.

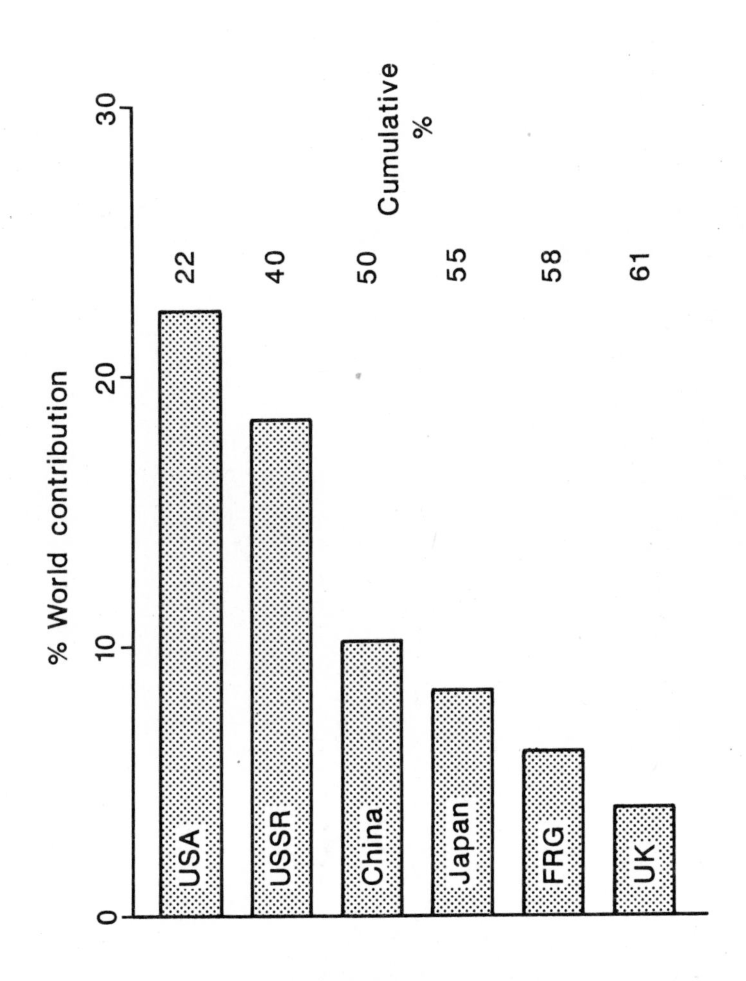

FIGURE 9
The top six contributors to CO_2 emissions.

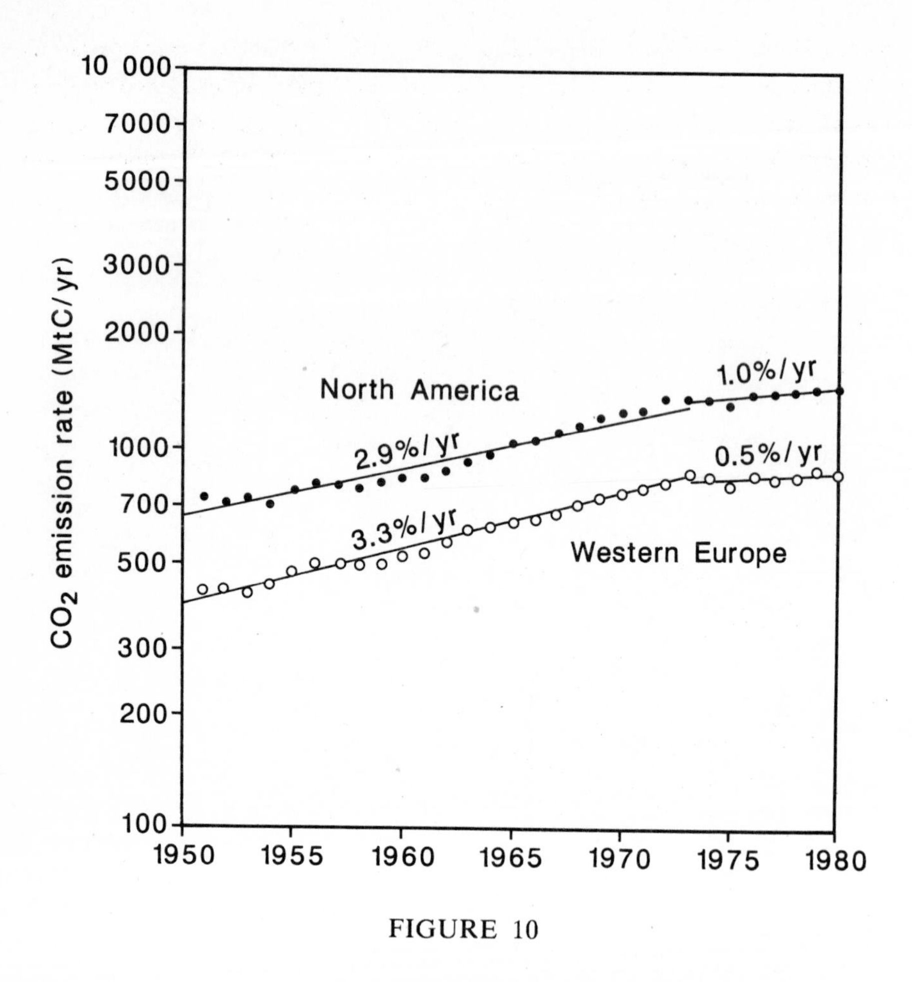

FIGURE 10

Fossil fuel CO_2 emissions in North America and Western Europe.

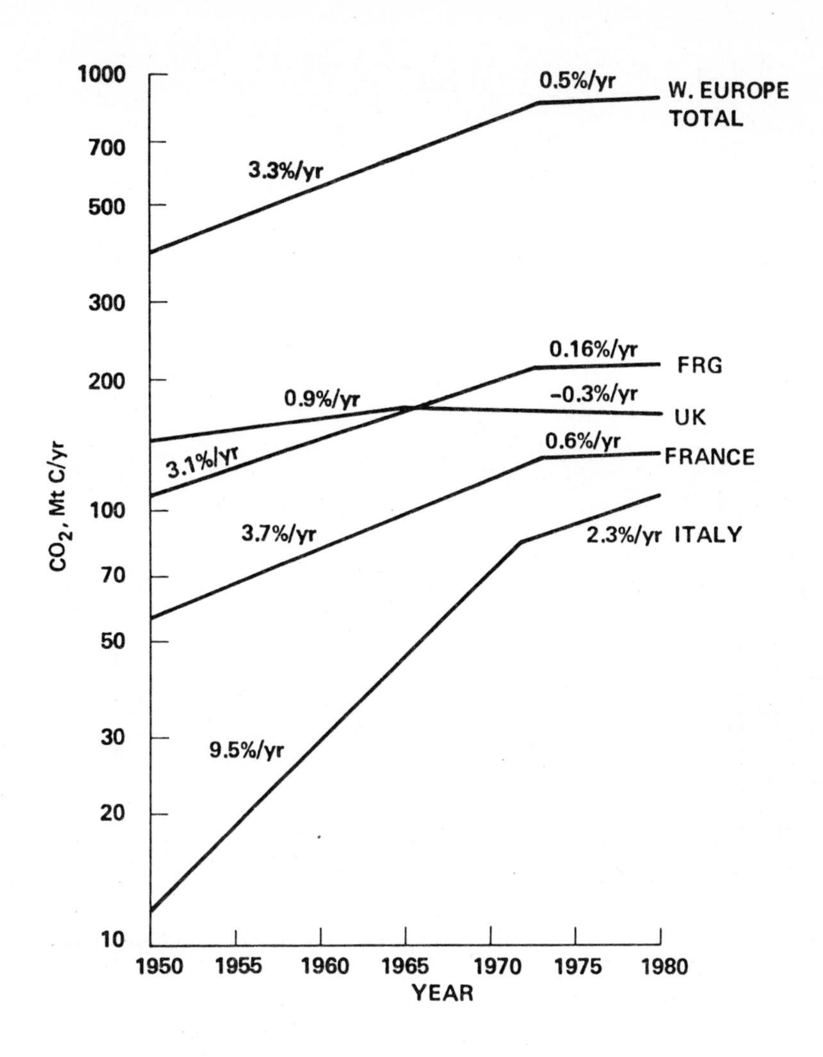

FIGURE 11

Fossil fuel CO_2 emissions in Western Europe

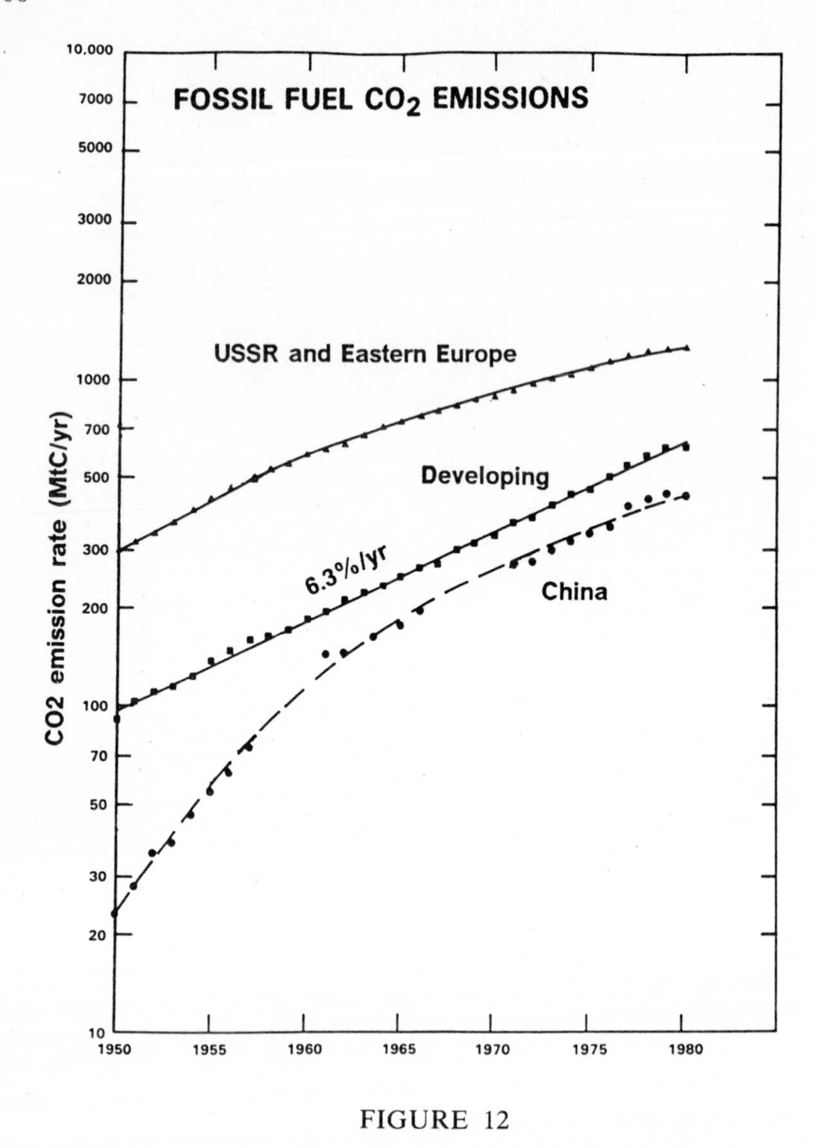

FIGURE 12

Fossil fuel CO_2 emissions from other selected parts of the world.

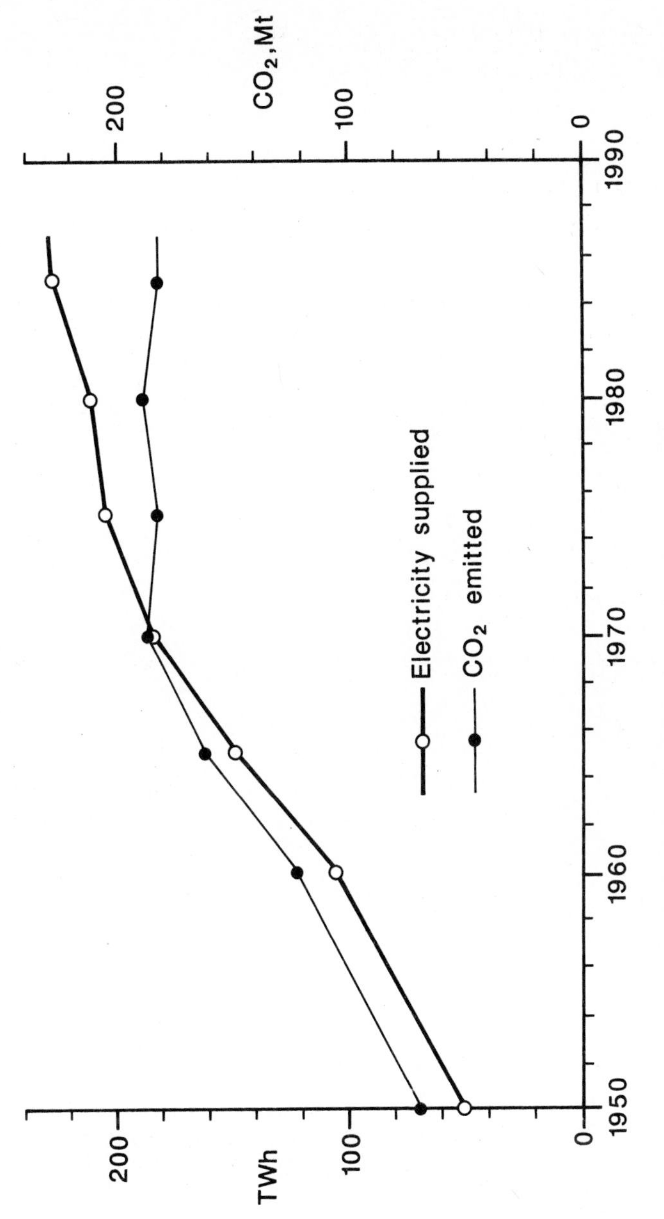

FIGURE 13 CO_2 emitted from electricity installations in the UK.

An indication of how the six biggest emitters in the world are contributing to CO_2 loading of the atmosphere is given in Figure 9 which shows that together they contribute 61 % of the world total of which the UK contributes around 3 %.

Trends in the emission of CO_2 from fossil fuel have shown a steady increase for a number of years (Figure 10). Until the oil crisis, North America and Western Europe were increasing their CO_2 emissions at around 3 % per year. It is interesting to note that their rates fell off substantially in 1973 - to 0.5 % per year in Western Europe. A breakdown analysis of countries in Western Europe given in Figure 11 shows that as long ago as 1965 the CO_2 emission trend for the UK became negative. Over the past 25 years CO_2 emissions in the UK appear to have been relatively constant.

In comparison an analysis for countries outside Europe (Figure 12) shows that the younger developing countries are increasing their CO_2 output by about 6.3 % per year and China and Eastern Europe almost as fast. Those trends are very substantial and very important.

In the UK, power stations account for about one third of CO_2 emissions but as shown in Figure 13 the trend in CO_2 emitted from electricity installations in the UK has been almost constant for 20 years, mainly as a result of improvements in the efficiency of generation and of course by a growing component of nuclear power.

What are the practical implications for electricity generation in the UK of some of the targets currently being referred to ? In 1988 the electricity industry produced 246 Terawatt hours and emitted 182 million tons of CO_2, the breakdown of which is given in Table 5. In 2005, if nothing were done at all to restrict demand (Table 6) 332 Terawatt hours would be produced. With the mix of fuels shown in Table 6 CO_2 emissions would be increased by 25 % to meet an increase in demand of 35 %.

TABLE 5

UK ELECTRICITY INDUSTRY STATUS - 1988

Total production 246 TWh
Total CO_2 emission 182 Mt

FUEL	Mtce
Coal	80
Oil	5
Nuclear	21

TOTAL	106

TABLE 6

UK ELECTRICITY INDUSTRY STATUS 2005 WITH UNRESTRICTED* DEMAND

Total production 332 TWh (1988 + 35 %)
Total CO_2 emission 227 Mt (1988 + 25 %)

FUEL	Mtce
Coal	97
Oil	9
Nuclear	31
Renewable	2

TOTAL	140

*Assumes 12.5 % end-use efficiency improvement over 1988

A restricted demand scenario is illustrated in Table 7, with the demand held constant at 246 Terawatt hours (the 1988 demand figure). This would make a 20 % cut in 1988 CO_2 emissions, but with major changes in fossil-fuel supplies. The nuclear component would be the same, but switching out of coal and into gas would result in coal consumption going down from an expected 97 million to 56 million tons. This would be a severe blow for the coal industry but not an unrealistic supply-side scenario in principle. It would, however, require very strong energy conservation measures to cut anticipated demand by 35 %.

TABLE 7

UK ELECTRICITY INDUSTRY STATUS 2005
WITH CO^2 REDUCTION BY RESTRICTED DEMAND

Total production 246 TWh (1988)
Total CO_2 emission 145 Mt (1988 - 20 %)

FUEL	Mtce
Coal	56
Oil	9
Gas	8
Nuclear	31
Renewable	2

TOTAL	106

With a more modest target, namely holding CO_2 emissions constant at their present level of 182 million tons per year, there could be some expansion of demand as indicated in Table 8.

TABLE 8

UK ELECTRICITY INDUSTRY STATUS 2005 WITH CO_2 HELD CONSTANT BY RESTRICTED DEMAND AND CHANGED FUEL MIX

Total production 300 TWh (2005 - 10 %)
Total CO_2 emission 182 Mt (1988)

FUEL	Mtce	Mtce
Coal	71	77
Oil	9	9
Gas	13	-
Nuclear	31	38
Renewable	2	2
	----	----
TOTAL	126	126

Although the fuel mix would change there would be various options. Gas or nuclear power would expand at the expense of coal; less so to the extent that renewables could expand very substantially. So holding electrical CO_2 emissions constant on that timetable should be possible in principle but it would mean a 10 % reduction in the demand anticipated for 2005.

Table 9 illustrates how difficult it is to do anything that isn't extremely serious for the economy and for social structures if demand is not restricted. With unrestricted demand, to meet the Toronto Conference target would require substantial expansion of nuclear power and a drastic cut-back of the coal industry. The need to restrict demand in some way or another is clearly underlined. Some reduction will happen anyway.

Achieving the rest will need positive acceleration which will require flows of capital investment that would not otherwise occur or would not occur so soon. Market intervention will also be required in some way to address the fact that present fuel prices do not reflect their relative carbon emission potential.

TABLE 9

UK ELECTRICITY INDUSTRY STATUS 2005
WITH CO_2 REDUCTION BY CHANGED FUEL MIX
(UNRESTRICTED DEMAND)

Total production 332 TWh (1988 + 35 %)
Total CO_2 emission 141 Mt (1988 - 22 %)

FUEL	Mtce
Coal	32
Oil	30
Gas	19
Nuclear	50
Renewable	9

TOTAL	140

In relation to global perspectives, at the moment the less developed countries (LDC) and China emit as carbon dioxide about 1.0 billion tons of carbon a year; the rest of the world some 4.0 billion tons, giving a total of about 5.0 billion tons. If the emissions of the LDCs and China continue to grow at their present rate, in 30 years time they will account for 6.0 billion tons. Even if the Western World were able to make the 50 % cut (i.e. to 2.0 billion tons) which is being talked about here, world emissions of would rise to 8.0 billion tons which is about double the present level.

Clearly another and absolutely vital dimension to this problem is the rate of growth of CO_2 emissions in the less developed countries as their economies grow. Looking 60 years ahead, if the 6.3 % growth continued and if there were enough fossil fuel supplies, the LDCs and China would be emitting about 40 billion tons of carbon or 8 times as much as the world is presently doing.

Clearly the equation cannot be balanced without the cooperation of the rest of the world. If the growth rates in the LDCs and China continue at their present rate for even 25 years, it would be necessary for the rest of the world to cut emissions of CO_2 to zero, simply to cap the present world total emission of 5.0 billion tons of carbon a year. Clearly the developing world and China must be major components in the balancing of this equation. The solution is essential but is extremely difficult to achieve. The world faces an enormous political problem.

Even now, on some estimates, deforestation and agricultural development accounts for something like 30 % of the total annual emissions of CO_2 (Figure 14). Up until 1965 the integrated emissions of CO_2 from deforestation have probably equalled emissions from fossil fuels. Good estimates are difficult to obtain, but probably even now at least 1.0 billion tons of carbon a year, possibly more, are entering the atmosphere from deforestation.

It seems that countries in the West have to do things that will enable the less developed countries and China to develop their economies without using so much energy - clearly a major challenge which has to be faced in addressing the greenhouse problem. Help must be given also to stop deforestation - the means must be provided for deforestation to be phased out and for reafforestation to take place. This would make an immediate and major impact on the present CO_2 balance.

If the countries concerned could be persuaded and assisted, to replant at the same rate as present deforesting, in 20 years something like, 2.0

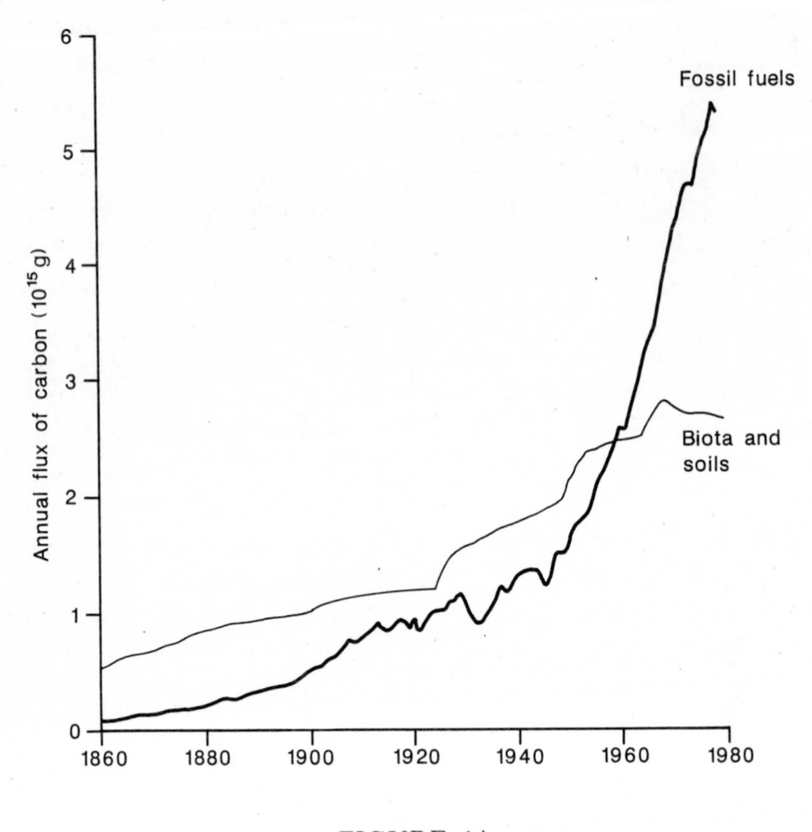

FIGURE 14

Increasing emisions of CO_2 from the use of fossil fuels as compared with that from biota and soils.

million sq km would have been replanted. That is an area about a quarter of the size of Brazil, but still a small area compared with the total area that has been deforested this century. During the time that these forests were developing, about 1.0 billion tons of carbon a year could be taken out of the atmosphere.

Reaforestation is not a permanent solution, it simply stores carbon in wood biomass. However, if that wood is used as a fuel to displace fossil fuel, carbon dioxide would be recycled rather than being added to. So, stopping deforestation and reafforesting could be an important component in the total portfolio of measures that the world has to take on this problem.

International agreements are going to be necessary, and getting them is going to be difficult. The harder and clearer the science, the easier it will be to get those difficult agreements.

POLITICS

6

INEVITABILITIES

Dr K von Moltke

Looking back over the last 15 or 20 years of the energy policy and environmental policy debates, there is a sense that the energy policy debate has been full of inevitabilities and remarkably little substantial change. Environmental policy todate has been full of quite extraordinary changes. The environmental community really is the community which is convinced that people can change: and in addressing the issue of climate change it is necessary to face full square that some very dramatic changes are going to have to occur.

By any traditional standard, it is clear that there are no political solutions to the problems of climate change. Reference has been made to uncertainties. Although there are some certainties in the science, there are many uncertainties which would be enough to undermine political conclusions if that were the intention. It seems to be that this is an extremely long-term issue, some 20, 30 or even 50 years and conventional wisdom tells us that political systems do not respond to issues with a timescale of more than four years. By *conventional* standards there are no solutions.

Global warming is the first issue where the original level of legislation is at the international level. Any purely national efforts are clearly futile and anybody who has been involved in international policy making over the last few years will recognise how extraordinary were the steps leading to the Montreal Protocol. Nevertheless, it still has to be accepted that it is certainly burdensome to try to deal with an issue where the original level of legislation is international. It is not just a matter of harmonising national policies. It is a matter of devising policies internationally, and to arrive at international implementation.

Basically it is a life-style issue which means changing the way people live; and not only the people in the Third World, but above all people in the Developed World. It is daunting to think that policies dealing with life-style issues need to be developed at an international level.

Since by *conventional* standards there are no political solutions to this issue, it is necessary to look for some *unconventional* standards. Anybody who has worked in the environmental community these last few years has to be an optimist, not only to start but also to continue. Political solutions may be found but at the same time involving some fairly dramatic innovations about the way in which affairs are conducted and the kind of things which can be agreed and discussed at the international level.

It is not relevant to get into the business of designing future societies. Perhaps it is accepted that what are known as command and control strategies may be necessary to reinforce certain basic messages, but they are not going to provide solutions. The consequences of such strategies in dealing with climate change issues are both socially and politically unacceptable. It is necessary to look at ways to change some of the basic signals which the policy making process is sending out to people and to companies. Some examples help to identify key issues.

Gross Domestic Product (GDP) has become firmly entrenched in national economic statistics, yet it is amazing how so arbitrary a figure can be so sanctified. Perhaps it is the very arbitrariness of it which makes it so beautiful. In the journal *International Environmental Affairs*, an article is to be published which recalculates Indonesian GDP between 1970 and 1984, taking into account only soil erosion, loss of forest cover and oil depletion. Indonesia is considered as one of the success stories among the less developed countries. However, if these alternative indicators of GDP are taken, then its GDP, instead of growing by 7.1 % as is commonly assumed, grew by only 4 %. Worse still, if other factors in terms of the loss of the natural resource base are factored in, it would be readily recognised that the Indonesian GDP growth remained well behind population growth, rather than outstripping it - as is generally assumed. Similarly, with net domestic investment in Indonesia under the same assumptions, instead of having annual average growth of over 11 % it would be just over 1 %. This illustrates the artificiality of the measure and the way in which the definition of GDP has to be re-thought.

Within existing political systems, there is the notion of a major shift in taxation away from income to raw materials. Basically what will have to happen sooner or later is a very substantial tax on either carbon or oil or oil equivalents. This tax must be revenue neutral, for the obvious political reasons, and would probably have to be introduced in a more or less co-ordinate way internationally. Although there have never been serious negotiations about taxes and the impact of taxes at an international level, but it is likely to be necessary if the world is to deal with the problems of climate change.

That economics of transport will have to be changed is an inescapable conclusion. What happened politically in the Netherlands during 1989 (see page 83) indicates some of the political issues which other countries will also have to face. Questions need to be answered such as: how can the total number of passenger automobile miles be decreased ? Many of the issues discussed in earlier chapters raise the questions: what does it all mean for our life-style ? How can the necessary change be achieved in a politically acceptable manner ? There are some pretty dramatic times ahead.

The concept is developing in some circles of a World Atmosphere Fund. This should not be confused with the notion of a Carbon Tax. There is a need for a World Atmosphere Fund because a lot of the research into global warming which is necessary must be funded internationally and some of it has to take place in less developed countries. It is true that the standards of research are international, but to gain acceptance of some of the unpleasant conclusions which will need to be drawn from this research, it is essential to have a strong research community in less developed countries. Unless this is done the outcome of the research will degenerate into a debate between the developed and the less developed world simply because of the difficulties of scientific communication. Funding this effort is the fundamental reason for the need of a World Atmosphere Fund. A tax on air travel (say $3 a ticket) would be perfectly adequate to finance such a fund.

Some of the other practical things that can be done now are:

- Change the criteria for environmental assessments to include climate change impact (ie the greenhouse potential of developments). A simple change, but with possibly substantial consequences.

- In assessing new and old chemicals include an assessment of their greenhouse potential. This can be done from first principles and built into the structure of the environmental legislation used.

- Do not allow false trade-offs in auto-emissions between *acidifying* pollutants and greenhouse gases. Combining stringent auto-emission standards with even more efficient fuel efficiency standards will give a package which is viable.

In general, the European Community has an important role to play in the climate change issue, a role which it has not played thus far because it has not been an effective force in energy policy. In adopting this role the Community will have to face some hard realities in connection with its own energy policy.

At the international level, the approach gaining widespread acceptance is to copy the success of the Vienna process. This is a process whereby a framework convention is set up followed by protocols. The convention framework establishes a timetable. The timetable set at the conclusion of the original Vienna Convention was an essential motor in achieving resolution of some of the conflicting issues which were present towards the end of the Montreal Protocol negotiations. The Vienna Convention model is a good one to follow. Though it may become necessary to amend the Vienna Convention from time to time (eg to link the stratospheric ozone depletion issue and the climate change issues), one way or another there is a need in all such debates to set up a framework convention followed by protocols.

The protocols may well pose all the difficulties, because the first issue is going to be the targets - carbon dioxide emissions, methane emissions, nitrous oxide emissions and emissions of CO_2 equivalents. Should targets be set for acceptable levels of carbon dioxide in the atmosphere or carbon dioxide equivalents or, in terms of acceptable rates of climate change such as 0.1° per decade ? Or perhaps targets in terms of acceptable sea-level rise ? The moment these issues are debated the difficulties in formulating specific protocols will be recognised. Protocols, again, imply life-style changes which everybody has to accept and this will require a substantial amount of time.

Finally, it is not just a matter of negotiating protocols, but of implementing them, and at an international level. This would seem to require an unprecedented amount of inter-penetration of national sovereignties. Countries will need to know so much more about what other countries are doing to implement these measures, with therefore an extraordinary level of openness and exchange of information as a precondition to handling these kinds of issues internationally. In the end there are in a sense feedback loops, in terms of life-style and the kinds of measures to be adopted.

As a general conclusion, it may be said there is a case for assuming that the outcomes if not the changes which will have to come, may well be radical. These changes may be as dramatic in their impact on society as was the micro-chip on electronics.

7

REALITIES

Jonathan Porritt

There is considerable inherent confusion surrounding the current debate about the Greenhouse Effect and the ways to deal with it; confusion which has to be a matter of considerable concern.

The simple fact is that global warming has delivered a terminal blow to our familiar reassuring way of looking at ourselves and the world: that familiar perspective is reflected in the rather crude reductionist division between separate government departments; it is reflected in the ways in which research projects are looked at as falling neatly into one scientific discipline or another; and it is reflected in the way in which domestic or international policy responses are looked at as if each one could be treated successfully in isolation. Global warming, quite simply, makes a nonsense of all of that and a lot else besides.

By the same token, global warming has also delivered an equally terminal blow to what is old fashioned, reformist environmentalism: the idea that there is, for every problem, some wonderful technical fix which can be summoned up out of a huge top hat and simply put in place with the right kind of political will and the right kind of investment. Technical fixing has been our exclusive response to environmental problems over the years. It has obviated the need to consider the far more profound social and political implications of the ways in which this planet is being abused whilst simultaneously denying two thirds of the human beings living on basic human rights. Environmentalism of that kind has a lot to answer for, in terms of the illusions from which we are all suffering today.

Paradoxically, therefore, the comfortable worlds in which Lord Caithness would seem to live at the Department of the Environment (DOE) and Jonathan Porritt might have been tempted to live at Friends of the Earth, have been simultaneously blown apart by the problem of global warming. Anyone who thinks that this is just another environmental issue to be addressed through the conventional medley of add-on, ad-hoc solutions is not living in the real world.

Most people are not prepared to accept such a radical departure from all that has gone before. It is this which leads to all sorts of intractable confusions, in the way in which we deal with global warming.

These confusions exacerbate the uncertainty that still exists in the science of global warming. They reinforce the doubt that lies in the mind of politicians about what they should be doing, how fast they should be doing it and what the political costs of it will actually be. When the Chief Scientist of the DOE tries to unravel policy out of that uncertainty (Chapter 3) the impossible is being attempted simply because politicians are only concerned with finding easy answers without fundamentally changing those factors which brought about the problem in the first place.

The only way out of the trap is to remove the confusion once and for all by implementing policies which promote *genuinely* sustainable development in a cost effective way, and which entail negligible ecological, political and social dis-benefits, should current predictions about global warming prove to be wrong. That is the base-line for an appropriate policy response on global warming.

On that basis, one comes to an inevitably harsh judgment about what is being done here in the UK at the moment. It is a period of extraordinary inconsistency; and if politics is the art of the possible, it is also the art of avoiding incoherence. On the one hand Lord Caithness, and Mrs Thatcher herself are quite deliberately talking up the problem in a way that must have surprised some of their own advisers and scientists.

On the other hand there is no real attempt being made to integrate different policies, in different departments, in order to match the gravity of the problem on which the community is being lectured with such regularity.

Look at some of those inconsistencies. The Energy Technology Support Unit talks about the need to achieve a 50 % reduction in CO_2 emissions in 30 years, and is looking to achieve 40 % of that reduction through energy efficiency measures. Many consider that to be a distinctly modest estimate of what is achievable, but nonetheless, let us accept these figures for the purposes of this discussion. In fact, even that very unambitious target is wholly unachievable within the existing parameters of government policy. Lord Caithness passed over (Chapter 1) without so much as a murmur the cuts in the Energy Efficiency Office's budget, from £25 million to £12 million. It is impossible to see how efforts to increase energy efficiency in this country can be supported by a cut in the budget of one agency that is actually able to do something about it.

Furthermore the Secretary of State for Energy is apparently none too pleased that the House of Lords should have seen fit to amend the Electricity Bill in order to give certain powers to encourage energy efficiency. Their amendment has been described as 'unworkable' and the Secretary of State has declared it will be reversed in the House of Commons. No effort has been made in that Bill to introduce the concept of " least-cost planning ". Within the Department of Energy itself, no effort whatsoever is being made to consider energy pricing let alone to assess the *true* costs of the different ways of generating electricity or providing energy.

There is no genuine policy development going on at the moment within Government to come to terms with their declared concern about global warming. One opportunity after another is simply passing by.

There is also the continued advocacy of the nuclear option as a means of doing something about global warming. On a small but important point it is actually wrong to say that nuclear power does not produce CO_2 - it does. If the nuclear cycle is followed all the way through from the mining of the uranium to the reprocessing of the spent fuel, nuclear power entails a very considerable CO_2 burden.

What this continued and indeed utterly redundant, advocacy of nuclear power reveals, is that people are still thinking in very old-fashioned terms. They are thinking about huge multi-megawatt plants to generate electricity in the old- fashioned way. Conceptually at Government level there is very little development about the ways in which electricity will be generated. That is in stark contrast to the attitudes of those who will take over the industry post- privatisation.

Friends of the Earth is not complacent about the extent to which global warming obliges everyone to look at *all* options. No environmental organisation's advice should be listened to unless it is prepared to assess those options on a regular basis given the changing circumstances in which everyone lives. There is a challenge here to all environmental groups; they will have to bear in mind the nuclear option and treat it fairly as an option - as rationally and dispassionately as in the past. The options for further research into nuclear power will indeed have to be considered, as will the acceptance of nuclear power itself, if it is able to meet the demands which have been laid upon it in the past.

Those demands are simple: it would have to be more cost- effective than other available ways of generating electricity; it would mean this industry would have to find a technical solution to the massive waste problem it now faces; it would mean it would have to come up with adequate answers to the problem of decommissioning; it would mean it would have to develop a so-called " fail-safe " reactor; and it would mean, finally, it would have to guarantee that " civil " nuclear materials could not be diverted into military uses. If scientists are able to achieve *all* of these things then every environmentalist has an obligation to consider the nuclear option as one small part of the answer to global warming.

The next major sector of concern is transport. In the Department of Transport itself, global warming is apparently an unknown concept. The Minister quite happily is contemplating an increase in traffic in this country of between 82 % and 142 % by the year 2025 ! Those are the figures from the last White Paper on inter - urban roads. How anybody in their vaguely right mind can contemplate a doubling of traffic on the roads of this country is beyond comprehension. How a Government can do so within the context of striving to combat global warming, is frankly unbelievable.

Compare all those inconsistencies with what is going on in Holland. The Government there has recently (1989) fallen because of an initiative to reduce the number of cars on the roads from 5.0 million to 3.5 million (not to double them, but to reduce them !), and to invest more than $6 billion in an integrated public transport system in order to deal with pollution from vehicle exhausts. It is a totally different situation from that which exists in this country: here there is endless green rhetoric and no policy development; in Holland there is dynamic policy development but obviously inadequate green rhetoric.

There are other inconsistencies: the question of CFCs and the speed with which they are phased out; agriculture policy and the continued promotion of inorganic fertilisers; the question of waste disposal and what happens to landfill sites. On practically every single issue the line taken falls to pieces as soon as the actual details are looked at. The charitable conclusion to be drawn from this is that briefings at Number 10 are simply inadequate.

It must be said that concerns in this country are often distressingly UK-centric. Even Britain's internationalism is disturbingly UK-centric! It is astonishing the way in which people talk about the Montreal

Protocol, surrounded by a rosy western glow as if it constitutes a lasting breakthrough to a new kind of internationalism. True, the Montreal Protocol has achieved a very great deal in terms of phasing out CFCs and other ozone depleting chemicals, but as many accept, it is not necessarily seen that way by the developing countries, who feel that it is being imposed upon them with none of the compensatory measures which would allow them to make up for the lost potential of the CFCs.

The Montreal Protocol, unknown to most people in this country, contains specific clauses on technology transfer and financial assistance. Those clauses have been totally disregarded by western countries. At the Helsinki Meeting, China and other countries were pressing for a special fund to help them to find substitutes for their ozone depleting chemicals. The Government of the UK, and those of several other developed countries, strenuously opposed that notion. If an International Convention on Climate Change is being considered it is necessary to start thinking about the ways in which technology transfer can be implemented and indeed additional financial assistance can be provided before pen is put to paper. If within the next 20 years in China and other LDCs a projected production increase from one billion tons of carbon dioxide up to 6 billion tons of carbon dioxide is contemplated then the speed of movement in this area is absolutely imperative.

There are many ways in which the developing world could be helped to leap-frog those CO_2 emitting technologies and other dirty technologies that have caused so much damage in the Western world. But specific financial methods have to be set in place in order to make it possible. The same is true in terms of limiting deforestation and encouraging reafforestation. The burning season in Brazil, over the course of a few months, brings with it the destruction of tens of thousands of square kilometres of wooded land. These fires are started deliberately by settlers and cattle ranchers in order to eke out some kind of agricultural subsistence from the so called " unproductive jungle ". There is no solution to that problem in Brazil or indeed in any other rainforest country until the issue of international debt has been dealt with - until those countries actually feel that the world economic order is going to give a fairer deal than it does at the moment, and that the vast burden being suffered through the repayment of interest and capital on this debt has been lifted. Until that day the forest will continue to go up in smoke.

A wholly new order of internationalism is being talked about. The Secretary of State for the Environment on several occasions has stated that any international convention must not override national sovereignty. This, of course, is an absolute nonsense. Significant areas of national sovereignty have already been surrendered through membership of the EEC; a plethora of environmental Directives have increasingly shaped policy here in the UK and we can all be thankful for that. The UK needs to face this one head-on. In ecological terms, Britain is not just for the British, nor is Brazil just for the Brazilians. Both Britain and Brazil have a role to play in terms of maintaining and protecting the global commons. Any Convention will entail significant inroads into classically conceived national sovereignty. Those inroads will only be possible if the gains are seen to outweigh the perceived loss of national sovereignty. It would help enormously if politicians ceased trying to sell the new found " green internationalism " through the defence of antediluvian concepts of national sovereignty. Such concepts will certainly have little meaning, post the deluge.

Lastly: beyond the accustomed domestic inconsistencies and beyond the international double standards there is the much more profound and difficult issue of the challenge that global warming makes to our very way of life. It has been blithely predicted (Chapter 4) that GDP in this country will double between now and 2020. Just think how Figure 5 would change if instead of worrying so much about energy per unit of consumption the whole question of the nature of GDP itself was addressed with equal enthusiasm. Redefining GDP (see also Chapter 6) is a precondition of being able to do anything about global warming.

There is a need to be pushing for a shift in taxation away from taxing income towards taxing energy and raw materials. Beyond that, there is a need to redefine the very concepts of progress and wealth.

This raises some prickly and uncomfortable issues, particularly for advocates of " green consumerism ". It is not just a question of consuming things in a rather more environmentally - sensitive way; it is actually a question of consuming *less* in order to add less to the problems of global warming. Much emphasis is given at the moment to whether people use unleaded petrol, or have got a catalytic converter on their car. But these things do not make a jot of difference to the problems of global warming. A motor- car with a catalytic converter still takes precisely the same amount of energy and raw materials to manufacture as a motor-car without a catalytic converter. If a doubling of motor-cars in this country between now and the year 2025 is seriously contemplated then their total impact on energy flows and global warming have to be given serious thought.

It is the same with aerosols. Friends of the Earth can be patted on the back for having persuaded the aerosol manufacturers to get rid of CFCs as propellants in their aerosols. Nonetheless, despite getting rid of CFCs in aerosol a major ecological breakthrough has hardly been achieved. Next year 850 million aerosol cans will still be produced in this country. Consider the energy use involved; consider the chemicals used as alternatives to CFCs, namely hydrocarbons such as butane and peutane; and, finally, consider the massive problems in terms of disposing of 850 million aerosols. Aerosols are *not* environmentally friendly and their continued manufacture is *not* sustainable, if that word is to retain any genuine meaning. Green consumerism should not be about feeling good when a catalytic converter has been fitted on your car or when you are smelling just as nice now that CFCs are not used in the aerosol. Green consumerism should be about feeling good when people have control over their lives such that they are able to walk or to cycle to work, are able to purchase reasonably priced organic food, are willing and able to eliminate all shoddy wasteful ephemera from their lives, to save energy whenever possible and so on. Green consumerism is as much about *not* buying things as buying things that are marginally more " environment - friendly ".

Such changes go infinitely further than anything that is on offer at the moment but even then, they don't really touch some of the difficult issues. The whole question of arms spending and anticipated concepts of military security, should feature very strongly in our concern about global warming. So too should the issue of population. Talk about global warming and talk about per capita CO_2 consumption means actually a need to remember it is *real* capita that needs to be talked about. Until the "environment movement" actually regains the courage to discuss population issues in the way that it once used to do, it is doubtful if they can make any particularly useful contribution to this problem either. Such a challenge is enormous. We are now on the threshold of introducing far more profound and far more visionary changes than some people may currently be contemplating. The problem of global warming has shattered all our old preconceptions, and will keep politicians and world leaders on a very uncomfortable hook until the root causes are sought out and honestly addressed.

DISCUSSION

Editors' Note:

The foregoing chapters have been edited, for the purposes of this book, from a recording made on the day of the **Global Warming : Global Warning** Conference.

The discussion which followed the presentation of these papers is given here as a verbatim record and has not been edited to conform to the presentation style of the earlier chapters.

Comment by:
Bruce Denness - Bureau of Applied Sciences

I should like to address a few comments to Dr Cattle concerning scientific issues. My concern is that we should not consider the greenhouse effect in isolation. The reason is that we might otherwise misinterpret everything that happens in the future as being just due to the greenhouse effect and consequently take precipitate actions which would not necessarily be justified. For instance, there have been variations in the global temperature pattern over the last hundred years or so other than those that can be attributed just to the greenhouse effect.

Figure 15 (a) shows the general increase of global temperature over the last century. Within that trend, as you earlier mentioned, there is a slight fall in temperature from about 1940 to 1970, an observation which we have to accommodate in some way. Conventionally we say that it is due to natural causes, one of the uncertainties. If the diagram had been extended a little further back it would have had to accommodate a global temperature rise of about 1.0°C to 1.5°C during the period 1830 - 1860; that was before the greenhouse effect existed, and its presence leads to a problem when it comes to interpreting future changes.

Conventional forecasts of likely greenhouse temperature increases suggest a maximum by the end of this century of about 0.4°C (e.g. Hansen *et. al.*, 1981: *Science* **213**, 957- 966). What would we do if we experienced a higher rise, perhaps as happened in the period 1830 to 1860? Would we say that was all due to the greenhouse effect ? Because if we did we would have to accept that it was a runaway effect: what kind of precipitate actions might we take in that case ? If we were to blame unknown natural causes what is the point of conventional climate forecasting models that are unable to differentiate reliably between natural and man-made changes ?

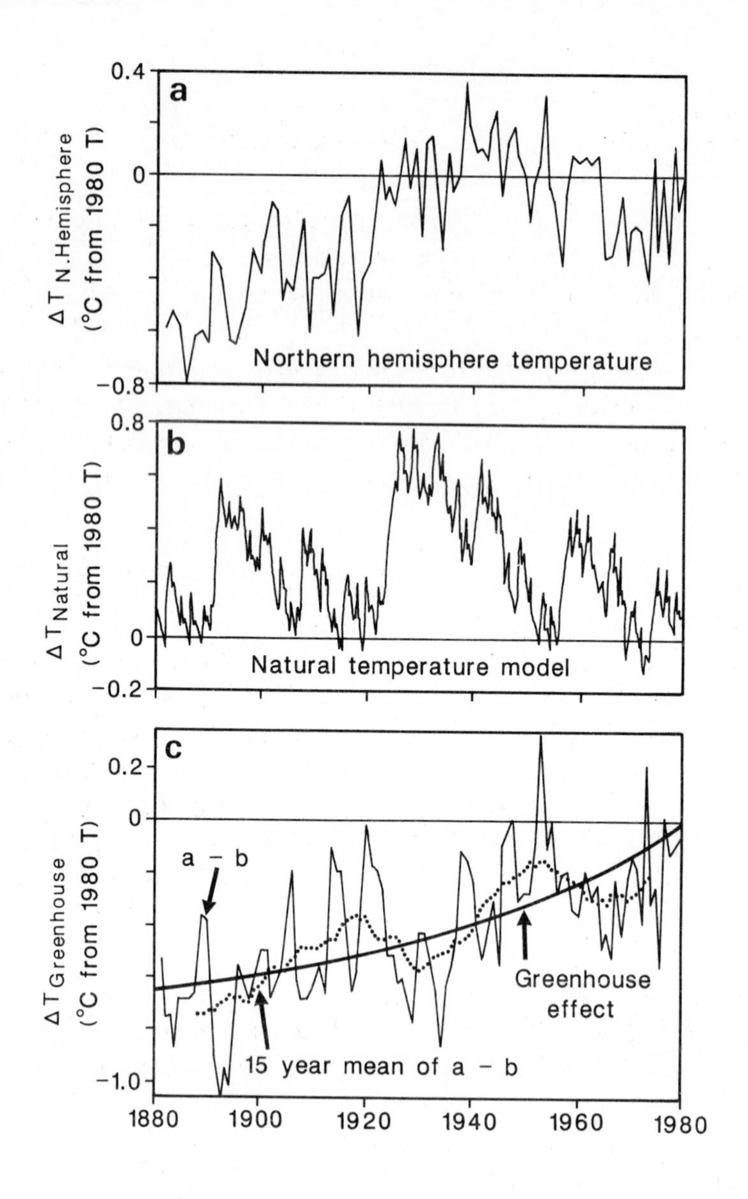

FIGURE 15

Global warming model proposed by Denness

I should next like to refer to my own forecasting model, which does indeed simulate natural as well as man-made global temperature change accurately. Based on earlier analyses (e.g. Denness, 1984: *Marine Pollution Bull.*, **15** (10) 355-362) Figure 15 (b) describes the model's representation of natural global temperature change over the last century. The natural component of the model is in the form of the relation:

$$G(t) = \sum_{n=N(T)}^{\infty} A(T).\ a^{n}.\ \sin\left\{b^{1-n}.\ \pi(\frac{t}{T})\right\}$$

which is zero-registered at time T_0 and in which:

G(t) is a time-based climate index, e.g. global temperature,
A(T) is the amplitude of a reference periodicity T,
N(T) is the reference integer for periodicity T,
a, b are absolute constants, here taken as 0.84 and 0.5 respectively, n is an integer, i.e. the reference number of a particular sine component and t is time in years.

Subtracting Figure 15 (b) from the observed global temperature (Figure 15 (a)) leads to Figure 15 (c) in which the raw data are indicated as (a) - (b). This should be the residual man-made component. The dotted line is a smoothed average of the raw data, the mean of which is the bold solid line. This is identical to the mean of conventional forecasts of the greenhouse effect and yet is derived from entirely different analyses.

The combination of man-made and natural components of this model accurately describe observed changes. It also embraces the 1.5°C rise of last century and goes on to forecast a global temperature rise of almost 1°C during the next decade. Various authors (e.g. Wigley *et. al.*, 1980: *Nature* **283**, 17-21; Klein, in: *Carbon Dioxide Review*: 1982 (ed. W.C. Clark), Oxford University Press, N.Y., 215-242) have established that many food-producing parts of the world, including the mid-west of the U.S.A., northwest Europe and southwest U.S.S.R., become drier as the world becomes warmer. Drought causes economic problems (Denness, 1984: *Energy Exploration and Exploitation*, **3** (1), 61-69). Therefore the 1990s should bring serious economic decline on a global scale as is suggested by the close inverse association between economic activity and global natural temperature as shown in Figure 16 for 20th century U.S.A., the economic engine of the world.

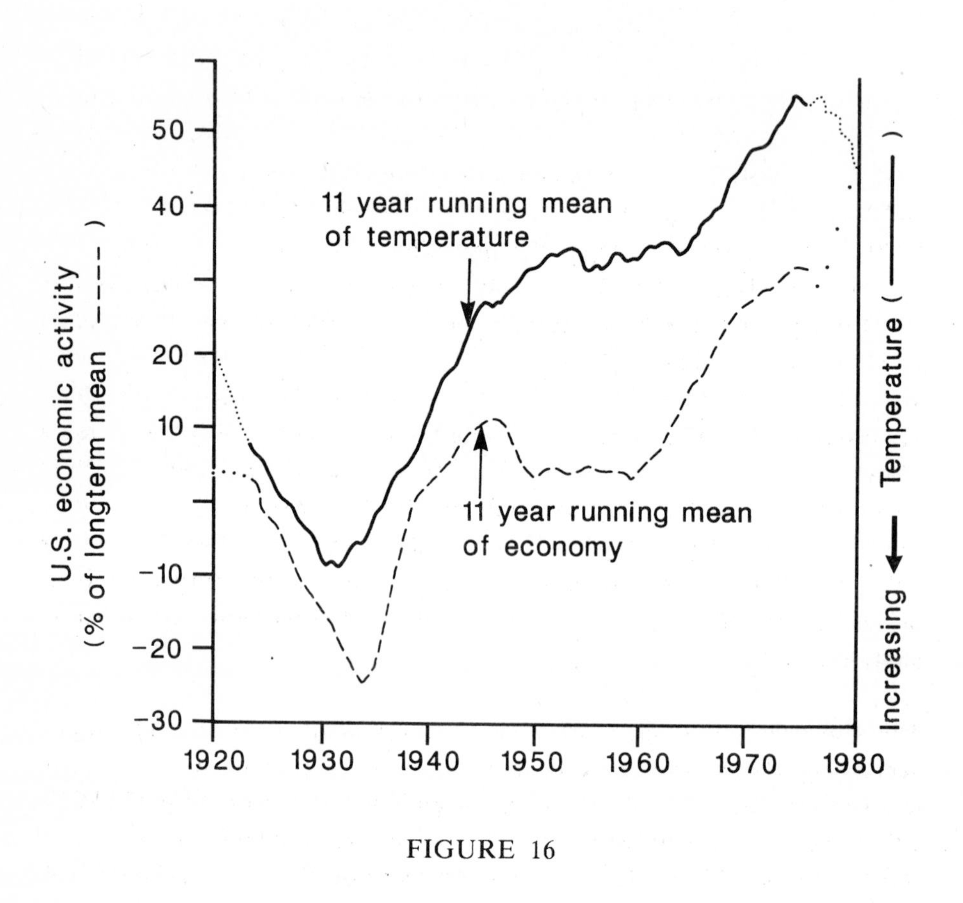

FIGURE 16

U.S. Economic activity and global temperature

Would Dr Cattle Comment on the way in which the Meteorological Office modelling accommodates natural changes ?

Reply by Dr Cattle

The problem of distinguishing the signal due to greenhouse gas-induced climate change against the natural climatic variability of the climate system is undoubtedly a fundamental and difficult issue, as Dr Denness points out. The natural variability of the climate system is inherently represented in the models which we run and comparing this with the natural variability of the observed climate system is an important component of climate research. The philosophy by which the model runs is carried out as follows. We first run the models forward in time for 'present day' climate for quite lengthy periods in order to derive the necessary statistics on variability. This gives us a so-called 'control simulation' which can be compared with the observed climate. We then carry out a parallel climate change experiment (for example doubling the atmospheric concentration of CO_2), and look at the differences between this run and the parallel control run. The significance of these differences must then be assessed against the model's natural variability using appropriate statistical tests. These enable statements to be made (usually expressed in terms of probabilities) as to how confident we are that the changes seen represent a real implied climatic change, rather than an expression of a change which has arisen as part of the natural variability of the model climate.

Bruce Denness

During the last ice-age the atmospheric CO_2 level was about 190 parts per million; at the beginning of the industrial revolution it was about 260 parts per million. This represents a rise in CO_2 levels of less than 40 % yet global temperature changed by about 6°C during that time.

However, we hear of needing to double CO_2 in order to cause a 3°C rise in temperature. In fact, the natural, much smaller proportional increase in CO_2 caused a 6°C rise in global temperature. It also caused a 100m sea-level rise. As conventional greenhouse forecasts envisage a rise of 4°C in a few decades, how many metres of sea-level rise does that imply either concurrently or in a future for which the present population could be held accountable ?

Reply by Dr Cattle:

As noted in my paper, on present estimates an equilibrium global mean rise of surface temperature of 4°C would imply a sea-level rise of 1.2 metres or so. CO_2 levels have certainly varied substantially on palaeoclimatic time-scales, the evidence for which is well documented in the ice core records. Such changes in CO_2 levels are likely to be associated with the ability of the ocean to take up CO_2. The solubility of CO_2 is temperature dependent, for example, in the sense that the lower the temperature, the more the gas can be dissolved, though ocean biology may also represent a significant factor. What has to be remembered, however, is that the onset and retreat of the ice ages (and the associated changes in sea level) is believed to have had, as a prime cause, the natural variations in the earth's orbital parameters which result in changes to the geographical and seasonal variations of the incoming solar radiation to the atmosphere. Such climatic changes are therefore induced by other than the changes in the greenhouse gas concentrations in the atmosphere alone. In looking at the overall changes from the last ice age to now we thus have to take into account both the warming due to increased CO_2 and that which has occurred due to the natural variations in the earth's orbit, as well as any other factors involved.

Comment by:
Dr Jeremy Leggett - Director of Science, Greenpeace UK

I have a question to do with positive feedbacks that arises from a worry that crept in as I listened to Drs Fisk, Cattle and Chester. There seems to be a sort of assumption that, as Dr Chester put it, global average temperatures can be allowed to double before there is really a need to worry. I doubt that we can rely on this. My concern comes back to the list of feedbacks considered in the general circulation models as described (in Chapter 2) by Dr Cattle. There is one major feedback left off this list which has to do with the effect of elevated temperature emissions themselves. The worst example of that involves methane which in high latitudes can be locked up in tremendous quantities in hydrate deposits. Reputable geologists in the United States are saying that in methane hydrates there could be as much as 10 trillion tons of carbon locked up. We have no way of knowing how much of that is vulnerable, but a Canadian geological survey team is now investigating the extent to which methane hydrates are stable; in 10-15 % of the 700 wells that have been drilled in the high north, there are indications of methane hydrates. This means that in principle, if global average temperatures go up just 1°C, they go up concomitantly higher at high latitudes and there is a risk of large quantities of methane being added to the atmosphere. Methane is a far worse greenhouse gas than carbon dioxide. As a result of such a positive feedback, we could be looking at figures for temperature far, far higher than we've heard considered here this morning. This is my concern, and I'd welcome the response of Dr Fisk to that.

Reply by: Dr Fisk

Dr Leggett, first in my rather rapid commentary, I think I actually touched upon the issue you mentioned. If you were looking at setting possible upper temperature rises, one of the uncertainties that really must be folded in is the extent to which the biosphere, rather than responding to the temperature rise, itself begins to contribute to greenhouse gases. You will also recall I said that methane is a gas with a relatively short lifetime, and the point may then be one of a disturbance of the biosphere, rather than a continual emission of methane. That would have to go in to the consideration of what sort of maximum temperature rise you would wish to tolerate given that you might not fully understand what the implications would be. There are other biosphere implications that you also touched on. We have today about 5 or 6 gigatons coming from anthropological sources into the atmosphere. That is a small proportion of the vast quantities of carbon which are annually swapped between the oceans, the land, and the air; and disturbances of those systems could of course change the atmospheric carbon dioxide and methane concentrations in any direction. It is fair to say that totting up the number of feedback mechanisms that have been proposed, there tend to be more that disturb the system towards increasing greenhouse gas concentrations, so called positive feedbacks, compared with the negative feedbacks which tend to decrease the overall effect. The most obvious example of negative feedback is that many plants in a carbon rich atmosphere will actually take up and embody more carbon, but there are other positive feedbacks and Dr Leggett has referred to some positive feedbacks which could operate in the other direction. Whether the 1°C he proposed is too narrow a band is perhaps a technical discussion that goes slightly outside the nature of this Conference, but the effects of the permafrost is certainly on the agenda as one of the issues to look at in the context of a maximum acceptable temperature rise.

Comment by:
Dr Tony Hart - World Disarmament Campaign UK

I was surprised that no-one, not even Jonathan Porritt, mentioned that the enormous wealth at present squandered in the world on armament manufacture will have to be diverted to solve the problems of the environment. Just recently I was at a conference where some Russians were talking about how they are converting arms factories to civil production. I was moved when one young man spoke about a missile factory being converted to making small windmills for less-developed countries. He said the future of the world depends on such countries having sustainable methods to meet their energy needs. That must be the way. I wonder if Mr Porritt might like to elaborate on that thought.

Reply by: Jonathan Porritt

Yes, I did refer to this, and I, like you, consider it to be enormously important. I think that we have to bear in mind, not only the costs and disbenefits of that massive arms budget in its own terms - namely in terms of its impact on human beings and political systems - but we have also to cost in the CO_2 impact of what a trillion dollar defence budget represents! However, let us be hopeful about things. Far more is happening now than ever before; there are genuine grounds for optimism that we are going to see significant cuts in defence budgets by the superpowers. Both of them, for their own domestic reasons, desperately need really swingeing cuts in their own military budgets. And if they can introduce these without causing too much upset to those political figures in their own countries that still hold such power, then I think they will be anxious, for domestic reasons as well as international reasons, to push on to further reforms. Let us hope there will then be a spin-off effect in terms of reduced military spending by developing countries.

Comment by:
Stewart Boyle - Association for the Conservation of Energy

My question is addressed mainly to Lord Caithness, but additional comments from Dr Dale and Jonathan Porritt would be welcomed. First of all, just to say in passing, that criticism of the use of the term 'fifth fuel' which also happens to be the name of our newsletter, cannot go without some comment. I think you are actually wrong when you say that energy cannot be conserved until there is a supply in the first place; this is quite incorrect. Because if in fact there is a better public transport system, if in fact people live closer to their work, and if houses were insulated better the need to have supplies in the first place would be negated. So I really refute the criticism of the use of the term 'fifth fuel'.

But the question itself is one that a number of speakers have concentrated upon - the fact that there appears to be an admission that market forces are failing to achieve proper energy efficiency and also that there is a need to bring in the proper pricing of fuels. What are the Government actually doing to bring this about? In a sense actually intervening is very much in contrast to the overall Government philosophy of allowing market forces to take their place. What proposals are being discussed at the moment to achieve proper pricing, to intervene where market forces are failing?

Reply by Lord Caithness

If you have a market, a market needs regulating far more than people think. People's conception that you can have a totally free market is wrong. You have got to have a regulatory framework within which the market operates. Now that has been distorted world-wide by some incredibly false subsidies on fuel which has led to a distortion in the price of fossil fuels in particular. It is high time that we all moved, not just in the United Kingdom, into a situation where the true costs and the true environmental cost of all fossil fuels and any other form of power is taken into account. Now if we do that ourselves it does put the United Kingdom at a huge disadvantage because we are a very coal-based economy still and therefore it has to be done in conjunction with other nations. We are certainly raising this issue internationally. One of the speakers made the point that the future is very much determined by the energy use in the developing world. I would equally say, the future depends very much on the strength of the economies of the Western world and the North Western world, because without the strength in the economy we cannot have the resources to help the Third World. Now that is absolutely vital. We must retain a healthy economy and should be cautious not to do anything that is going to adversely affect it unnecessarily and therefore which will militate against us helping the Third World in ways we can. What we can do is for all of us to realise that there has been false economy in subsidising certain fuels, and that within a proper pricing structure, the market has an important role.

Comment by:
Pat Saunders - Quaker Peace and Service

I would like to comment on Dr Fisk's methods of looking at policy issues in the context of the level of increased greenhouse gases that we might be willing to tolerate. I think he mentioned some German study that had described a 2°C temperature increase as tolerable. I understand that UNEP studies have shown that a 1°C increase in Uganda would make it impossible for them to cultivate coffee (robusta) and that a 1.0 metre increase in ocean levels would flood portions of the Nile and Bangladesh Deltas displacing 10 and 15 million people respectively. So it seems to me that unless we in the rich industrial countries, who have been responsible for the lion's share of the problems so far, are actually willing to bear the full costs of enabling such countries to cope with the consequences of our pollution and waste, then the levels of temperature increase that we are willing to tolerate should be considerably less than that suggested.

Reply by: Dr Fisk

The upper tolerable temperature cannot be lower than 0.7°C because on the most pessimistic projection that is the sort of temperature rise that is already in the pipeline (as Dr Cattle explained). I would assume that if 0.7°C were to have adverse consequences the international community would as is usual in cases of climate- based disasters stand by those who suffered. I do want to stick with either 1°C or 2°C. The speaker has made a very pertinent point that these figures are one of the most important parts of the study by the Intergovernmental Panel on Climate Change. We must also bear in mind that not only may there be an effect on those who are directly trading in a particular commodity, but there may also be a knock-on effect on those who buy it. I take the point made from the floor as very much underlining my case that the impact studies are a crucial part of moving forward.

Comment by:
David Cope - UK Centre for Economic and Environmental Development

I would like to congratulate Jonathan Porritt on what I thought was an excellent close to the formal presentation, particularly towards the end when he mentioned the fact that the environmentalist movement has to get to grips with the whole question of population. I think the way that area has been ignored over the past decade has been verging on the supine. One knows why of course, because the far left and the far right came together to squeeze the whole question of world population. However, I do not want to dwell on that.

It was his remarks about nuclear power that fascinated me, because, although he tried to discount them, I did find them significant. Jonathan, you raised some formidable requirements that nuclear power would need to meet before you could see it becoming potentially acceptable. One of these was, I think, the separation out of the civil and military components. This is technically achievable tomorrow but it is essentially a political question about which people would have different views. Looking at the technical issues which you have raised, things like waste disposal, the design of new types of reactors etc., would you not accept that does imply some continuing research and development in the field of nuclear power ? I would be interested to hear your comment on the level of that. Before you do so, a frequent response to this sort of question is to say, " ah ! but 40 years of massive investment has gone on in nuclear power with very little to show for it " and maybe some would agree with that but in a sense that is irrelevant, that is a sunk cost, and if nuclear power does potentially have the ability to meet those criteria you lay down, it does seem to me to imply that one does accept some continuing at least of research and development in that particular form of energy.

Reply by: Jonathan Porritt

Different environmental organisations have a different view on this. It does strike me that any environmental organisation that claims to be offering dispassionate advice to people about the enormously complex issues of how we meet our energy needs in the future, has to accept the obligation of offering dispassionate advice on the latest state of play in *every* technology, and that includes the nuclear technologies. If they are not doing and they are merely saying nuclear is "evil" by definition and therefore beyond the pale of our consideration, I cannot see on what grounds they can offer advice to anybody. I have always argued that quite honestly. When we talk about the extent to which that entails a continued commitment to nuclear research , the answers to the questions it raises cannot emerge without such research, albeit at a far lower level than before. We have had such disproportionate funding of nuclear-based research and development over the last 40 years as to entail a massive opportunity cost for the whole of the rest of the energy sector in this country and in the developing world. We have lost out on one technological opportunity after another because of our obsession with nuclear power. It is a burden we are carrying the cost of even now.

So as far as I am concerned, nuclear power is one technology amongst all the rest of them and, in my opinion, infinitely less likely to come up with the goods than many others. This means a massive shift of resources into renewables and more efficient generating technologies.

Comment by:
Malcolm Harper - United Nations Association

My comment to the Minister is to say how profoundly I disagree with his analysis of the relationship between the state of the British economy and our ability to help the developing world. We have had 10 years we are told, of sound economic management. Yet over those 10 years official British aid has reduced to a paltry 0.28 % of GNP. The equation does not make sense to me.

The question I would like to ask is this. In terms of both global warming and related issues, what immediate steps should be taken to : (a) strengthen and expand the role and functions of the United Nations Environment Programme, and (b) secure greater adherence within the United Nations family to the system-wide medium-term environment programme ?

Dr von Moltke

I think the question of what to do to strengthen the United Nations Environment Programme is very much on the agenda. The slight increase in resources which have been forthcoming, and I say that advisedly, is encouraging, but it does not resolve some of the structural issues. I personally think that one of the best proposals on the table right now is to create a permanent Environmental Committee of the Security Council, and to make UNEP the secretariat to that Committee. That would resolve many of the current structural difficulties within the United Nations system. I have always argued that the resources needed in this area have been orders of magnitude too small.

Comment by:
Nigel Haigh - Institute for European Environmental Policy

I have one question for Lord Caithness and Dr Fisk, and another for Dr von Moltke.

Would either the Minister or Dr Fisk comment on the resolution that the Council of Environment Ministers of the European Community are expected to adopt on Thursday on the greenhouse effect or global warming. Will it lay the broad outlines of the European Communities' approach to any forthcoming convention, and will it make any reference at all to the conclusions of the meeting recently called at the Hague by the French Prime Minister and the Dutch Prime Minister.

My question to Dr von Moltke is whether from an American point of view he will comment on American reaction to that meeting at the Hague.

Reply by: Dr Fisk

As you will appreciate, that document has not yet formally gone in front of the Environment Ministers so it really does rather fall to the bureaucrats who have negotiated the text so far to answer your question. The text, of course, principally addresses a work programme which allows the European Commission itself to look at this issue. Particularly important to the United Kingdom is a commitment by the Commission to look over existing Directives, many of which now need quite serious revision. Indeed, there is a need to look more systematically at the way in which this issue addresses Europe and the European economy. That is the thrust of the resolution. It is not specifically addressing conclusions which have come from other international meetings, either Toronto, London or the Hague, but it is directed specifically at a future work programme that the Commission have in mind. That programme fits in very neatly and takes full account of the work that is appearing in the Inter-Governmental Panel on Climate Change. Probably the right way to approach the text as it is likely to go in front of European Ministers is as one looking forward to the report of the Inter-Governmental Panel on Climate Change rather than looking back at a number of developments that have occurred in getting the political momentum to this stage.

Reply by: Dr von Moltke

It is difficult to comment about the Hague declaration from a North American point of view because one has to bear in mind that the Canadians invented the silliness of the law of the atmosphere. Also the United States came up with a proposal for a workshop at an advanced stage of negotiations in Geneva at the Inter-Governmental Panel on Climate Change a couple of weeks ago. Neither of which really took into account the needs and priorities of international negotiation, but really responded to a variety of domestic needs. I would see the Hague Conference in the same context and these kind of events are unfortunate; there was something similar done by the West German Government at the Munich Conference, in the context of negotiations on acid rain - a totally unnecessary event from my point of view. So the challenge then becomes the unfortunate necessity for everybody to find ways to justify what was done. I think the particular proposal of taking a sub-committee to the Security Council really responds to all of those needs very neatly. I would suggest that that fully meets all the requirements of the proposals made at the Hague.

Comment by:
Tessa Robertson - World Wide Fund for Nature - UK

I wanted to say how much the WWF welcomes the recent decision by the UK Government to agree to the European Commission's revised proposal on small car emissions, which will of course, mean the introduction of three-way catalysts. But I would like to say to the Minister that while it is certainly true that three-way catalysts cannot remove carbon dioxide from vehicle emissions, they do have a function indirectly in removing other greenhouse gases. For example, by removing carbon monoxide they remove a scavenger of hydroxyl radicals in the atmosphere, which are of course a sink for methane. What I would really like to say to the Minister, however, is that we see the introduction of three-way catalysts as a very short-term option. They will have great benefits in terms of acid emissions, but what we would like to see now is the introduction of fuel efficient vehicles. We do know that a number of manufacturers, particularly in Europe, have actually got prototype vehicles which can reach fuel efficiencies in excess of 100 miles per gallon. Now there seems no reason why we have to always concentrate on the lean-burn engine when we could bring in these prototypes, which have features such as much lighter construction materials, continuously variable transmissions; this kind of thing. I would like to ask the Minister whether the UK Government has any plans to bring in legislation or any other commitment to introduce these vehicles into the UK, or indeed to make any proposals to the EEC ? I am thinking, for example, along the lines of what has happened in the US since the 1970s, where legislation has actually caused a doubling of the fuel efficiency of vehicles. We are seeing the same thing in Japan, and again in Sweden there is a voluntary agreement.

Reply by: Lord Caithness

I am delighted to hear you say three-way catalysts are just an interim solution - I think they are too. They do not address all the problems and it is I think one of the hallmarks of failure of the Community that when they have addressed problems they have not looked at all the effects and we are quite clearly wrong not to take into account fuel efficiency or carbon dioxide. There are lots of different ways of doing this. We are not hooked as a government on lean-burn, we are committed to a market-place that can produce alternatives. If people can produce alternatives other than lean- burn that achieve the same result of better fuel efficiency that would be, to my mind, something that is worth supporting. I think that the Germans could set a very good lead in the interim as well as having three-way catalysts they can reduce their speed limit on autobahns.

Comment by:
Ellen Teague - The Catholic Fund for Overseas Development

My question is addressed to Lord Caithness. How would you define progress ? What would your notion of progress be bearing in mind the demands of sustainable development ? I am not just thinking in terms of a hundred years, but in terms of thousands, millions of years and within the constraints of demands of justice for the Third World poor. How do you understand progress within those constraints ?

Reply by: Lord Caithness

That is a vast question, and the most difficult questions are always the shortest ones are they not ? Progress can be defined in a number of ways. What we must never lose sight of, and I think this has come over quite clearly today, is that climates change naturally and there has always been a natural change in the climate. What we have got to do is take the man-made element out of that and say what we could do to reduce its effect. We must look at not only the effects on the climate of course, but also at every sort of pollution, every effect on the environment for which man is responsible. Jonathan Porritt has mentioned the rise in population. If we look at the graph of what is going to happen to the world's population, add to that the loss of top soil, desertification, there are real problems ahead. But I remain of the view that climate is the biggest because it affects all of those. Man is a polluter by nature; we have got to change all of that, and we have to become a great deal more aware of the environment in everything we do whether it is building a road, diverting a stream, building a house or some of the very much more complicated things that at the moment require an environmental impact assessment. It is a huge area that needs to involve everybody in the world because what we are doing now, China with a quarter of the world's population, could be doing with vastly more detrimental effects in the future. So we have to bring everybody on board.

Comment by:
Michael Grubb - Royal Institute for International Affairs in London

I would like to raise two brief points on the science and then a question on policy issues. We have been left with a somewhat confused picture of the scientific situation, perhaps more so than necessary. In Dr Cattle's talk he mentioned three possible reasons why models disagree to some extent with what has been observed over the last century or so. My first point is that in addition to those which also included natural variability, there are man-made inputs over the last 100 years, other than greenhouse gases. I am referring to things like aerosols (not the spray can) in the scientific sense of small particles and to sulphur emissions which can act as nuclei for clouds - which also will tend to lead to a global cooling. So we have been interfering with the atmosphere in ways that would offset any greenhouse effects which is a fourth reason for disagreement on current observations. The second point is that given that the climate is so variable in terms of temperature, precipitation, and so forth, we should look for signs of greenhouse warming somewhere else, such as the longer-term stores of the ocean, or in the tundra. There was a paper about six weeks ago (I believe in *Nature*) which allegedly contained an account of very detailed measurement of ocean temperatures over the last decade or a little more. These showed warming of 0.1° per year; an extraordinary rapid rate of warming in terms of the things we have been talking about. That is where one would expect to see signals most clearly and I would be grateful for any comments on that because I was very surprised at the figure.

The question, on the policy side, is this: two speakers have mentioned a shift of taxation from income to resources almost as a throw-away line. That strikes me as having enormous implications. I would be interested to know if the UK Government is looking at that or if studies have been made on economic impacts of such a policy, both nationally and (as was suggested) in international terms where one is talking about possibly massive financial resources and some international basis of control.

Reply by: Dr Cattle

In commenting on the first part, I would agree with the speaker that the sea surface temperatures of course are very useful indicators of climate change. The results which he referred to are, I believe, analyses of global warming from satellite-derived sea surface temperatures, compared with that derived from conventional data sources such as ships and buoys, over the period 1982-88. One has, of course to be cautious about inferring longer-term trends from relatively short period records and we are currently taking a close look at these results at the Meteorological Office. As well as the sea-surface temperature, the ocean structure beneath the surface may also provide a useful indicator of climate change. The *World Ocean Circulation Experiment* which is due to take place in the 1990s has already been referred to and will provide an important contribution to studies of climate and climate change in this respect.

Reply by: Dr von Moltke

Although I do not think that the question was addressed to me I would like to comment on the grounds that I made the initial comment about the shift of taxation. What I said was that it seemed to me we were going to have to discuss revenue neutral changes in taxation from income either to carbon emissions or to some form of fuel tax. I think the revenue neutral aspect is important, but it is not for me to comment whether it is being discussed in this country or not. I would be interested to know. In North America this has become a matter of serious discussion; I cannot pretend it is about to be enacted, but it is being seriously considered.

Lord Caithness

Could I just pick that point up, because it rather follows on from what Tessa Robertson said earlier. I do not think that I fully answered her point. Yes we will be pressing in Europe for a look at all fuel efficiencies and this might well affect taxes and other things. But I do not think that we fully understand yet what we should be doing because of the limited amount of hard science available. As we get more information so we will be able to make better decisions.

Comment by:
Bob Everett - Open University

The first thing I wanted to say is that I have just been to a conference in Sweden (as have several other people in the audience) given by the Swedish State Power Board. Basically they set themselves the seemingly impossible task of not increasing CO_2 emissions, of not developing new hydropower and of phasing out nuclear, which is half of their electricity production. At the conference they expected to be told this was impossible, but a very enthusiastic bunch of people came along, especially the Americans, to tell them that new technologies would make this quite possible and that they could have their cake and eat it. A quite magnificent 1,000 page book was produced on electricity and energy use efficiency and new-generation technologies which contain an awful lot of stuff of which I had never previously heard. I heartily recommend it to anybody. (*See Bibliography* eds.)

My question is on the fact that combined heat and power generation (CHP) has not really been mentioned. I believe it is a technology which is so important that it requires its own separate slot. Denmark has used nation-wide CHP to actually carry out a shift from oil to coal. The studies in this country (carried out by none other person than Walter Marshall, now Head of the CEGB), showed that CHP was very viable. I would like to ask what is the role of large-scale CHP in this country, and what is the Government going to do to implement a market for heat ? It is all very well having a free market, but if the market does not exist in the first place it cannot function and one of the recommendations of the Select Committee on CHP (in 1983 perhaps) was that there ought to be a Heat Board and that a market for heat should be set up.

Reply by: Dr Chester

That was an excellent conference, one of my colleagues contributed to it. They certainly came up with some very imaginative thinking. There are obviously a number of things you can do. They all require an increased flow of capital or an earlier flow of capital than would otherwise have been required. That is really why CHP has not penetrated - there was generally a cheaper way of providing the heatflow. Normal market mechanisms will not do the trick. On the particular point of conservation though, it may get you off the present growth curve, but you cannot get the benefit over and over again. You have ultimately to address the question of Third World growth and the issues that Konrad von Moltke raised in his paper.

GLOSSARY

Brundtland Report:

Report of the World Commission of Environment and Development set up by the General Assembly of the Unite Nations in 1983 chaired by Nrs. E. H. Brundtland, Prime Minister of Norway.

Energy Technology Support Unit, Department of Energy,

Is based at the Harwell Laboratory, Oxfordshire, UK.

Environmental Council:

of the European Community, Brussels.

Hague Declaration:

Made in The Hague, Netherlands, March 11, 1989.

Helsinki:

First Meeting of the Conference of the Parties of the Vienna Convention for the Protection of the Ozone Layer, April 26-28, 1989.

First Meeting of the Parties to the Montreal Protocol on Substances that Deplete the Ozone Layer, May 2-5, 1989.

Intergovernmental Panel on Climate Change (IPCC):

set up in November 1988 as an intergovernmental mechanism to study all issues related to climate change; brought into being by joint decisions of the World Meteorological Organisation and the United Nations Environment Programme. Secretariat is in Geneva - staff of 43. Operates through three Working Groups.

Journal of International Environmental Affairs :

Published by University Press, New England, USA.

London:

Saving the Ozone Layer Conference hosted by the British Government, March 5-7, 1989

Montreal:

Conference of Plenipotentiaries on the Protocol on Chlorofluorocarbons to the Vienna Convention for the Protection of the Ozone Layer, September 14-16, 1987.

Munich:

Meeting called by the Government of the Federal Republic of Germany on Acid Rain.

Sweden:

Electricity Conference organised by the Swedish State Power Board, Gottenburg, June 1989.

Toronto:

International Conference on the Changing Atmosphere, June 27-30, 1988.

Vienna:

Convention on the Protection of the Ozone Layer, Final Act, 1985.

BIBLIOGRAPHY

This bibliography includes only a selection of published works on the greenhouse effect and global warming. They have been selected by the editors as a representative cross-section of the many publications that are available.

BEIJER INSTITUTE, 1989 *The Full Range of Responses to Anticipated Climatic Change.* Beijer Institute, Stockholm. 182 pp.

BLEVIS, L.D., 1988 *The New Oil Crisis and Fuel Economy Technologies: Preparing the Light Transportation Industry for the 1990s.* Quorum Books.

BOYLE S., 1989 *Solutions to Global Warming: Questions and Answers.* ACE.

BUNYARD P., 1987 The significance of the Amazon basin for global climatic equilibrium, *The Ecologist*, 17 (4-5) 139-141

CHANDLER, W., GELLER, H. & LEDBETTER, M., 1988 *Energy Efficiency: A New Agenda.* The American Council for an Energy-Efficient Economy.

CHEN R. S. & M. L. PARRY (Eds.) 1987 *Climate Impacts and Public Policy.* IIASA Laxenburg, Austria. 54 pp.

CLARK W.C. & MUNN, R. E. (Eds.) 1986 *Sustainable Development of the Biosphere.* Cambridge University Press. 491 pp.

CONROY, C. & LITVINOFF, M. (Eds.) 1988 *The Greening of Aid.* Earthscan.

DELFT HYDRAULICS 1989 *Criteria for Assessing Vulnerability to Sea-Level Rise : a Global Inventory to High Risk Areas.* Delft Hydraulics, Amsterdam. 51 pp.

DEPARTMENT OF THE ENVIRONMENT, 1988 *Possible Impacts of Climate Change on the Natural Environment of the United Kingdom.* London

FLAVIN, C., 1989 *Slowing Global Warming : A Worldwide Strategy.* Worldwatch Paper 91.

FLOOD, M., 1987 *Energy Without End: the Potential for Renewable Energy.* Friends of the Earth, London.

GIBBONS, J. H., BLAIR, P.D., & GWIN, H. L. 1989 Strategies for energy use, *Scientific American,* 261 (3) 136 - 143

GLANTZ M. H. (Ed.) 1988 *Societal Responses to Regional Climatic Change : Forecasting by Analogy.* Westview Press. Boulder, Colorado. 428 pp.

GOLDEMBERG, J., WILLIAMS, R., REDDY, A. & T. JOHANNSEN, 1988 *Energy for a Sustainable World.* World Resources Institute, Washington, DC.

GOREAU T. J., & DE MELLO, W. Z., 1988, Tropical deforestation : some effects on atmosphere chemistry, *Ambio,* 17 (4) 275-281.

GRAUMLICH L. J. & BRUBAKER, L. B. 1986 Reconstruction of annual temperature (1590-1949), *Quaternary Research,* 25, 223-234.

GREGORY S. (Ed.) 1988 *Recent Climatic Change : A Regional Approach.* Belhaven Press. London. 326 pp.

GRIBBIN, J., 1988 *The Hole in the Sky : Man's Threat to the Ozone Layer.* Corgi, London 160 pp.

HARRINGTON J. B. 1988 Climate change : A review of causes, *Canadian Journal of Forest Research,* 17 (11) 1313-1339

HULM, P., 1989 *A Climate of Crisis : Global Warming and the Islands of the South Pacific.* Association of South Pacific Environmental Institutes, Port Moresby, Papua New Guinea.

IDSO S. B., 1988 Greenhouse warming or Little Ice Age demise : a critical problem for climatology, *Theoretical Applied Climatology,* 39(1) 54- 56

JOHANSSON, T., BORTLUND B., & R. K. WILLIAMS (Eds) 1989 *Electricity, Efficient End Use and New Generation Technology and Their Planning Implications.* Lund University Press, 986pp.

KARL, R. T., & QUAYLE R. G. 1988 Climate change in fact and in theory : are we collecting the facts ? *Climate Change* 13 (1) 5 - 18

KEEPIN, B. & KATS, G., 1988 Greenhouse Warming, Comparative analysis of Two Abatement Strategies. *Energy Policy,* December 1988.

KRISTENSEN, T. & PALUDAN J. P. 1988 *The Earth's Fragile Systems : Perspectives on Global Change.* Westvierw Press, Boulder, Colorado. 109 pp.

LAMB, H.H., 1988 *Weather, Climate and Human Affairs.* Routledge & Keegan

LANGEWEG, F. (Ed.) 1989 *Concern for Tomorrow : A National Environmental Survey, 1985 - 2010.* National Institute of Public Health and Environmental Protection, Bilthoven, Netherlands. 344 pp.

MATHEWS, J. T. 1987 Global climate change : toward a greenhouse policy, *Issues in Science and Technology*, 3 (3) 57 - 68.

MAXWELL J. B., & BARRIE, L. A. 1989 Atmospheric and climatic change in the Arctic and Antarctic, *Ambio*, 18 (1) 42-49.

NATIONAL RESEARCH COUNCIL (USA) 1987 *Responding to Changes in Sea Level : Engineering Implications.* National Academy Press, Washington, D. C. 148 pp.

POLLOCK S, C., 1988 *Renewable Energy: Today's Contribution, Tomorrow's Promise.* Worldwatch Paper No. 81, January 1988.

RENNER, M. 1988 *Rethinking the Role of the Automobile.* Worldwatch Paper 84, June 1988.

SONKA S. T. & LAMB P. J. 1987 On climate change and economic analysis, *Climatic Change*, 11 (3) 291 - 312

TIMBERLAKE, L., 1986 *Africa in Crisis.* Earthscan.

TITUS J. G. 1986 Greenhouse effect, sea level rise, and coastal zone management, *Coastal Zone Management Journal*, 14 (3) 147-171

UNEP 1987 *Man and the Atmosphere : Climate Change, Ozone Layer, : Sources of Information and Bibliography.* UNEP, Nairobi 387 pp.

UNEP/GEMS. 1987 *Greenhouse Gases.* Environment Library, No. 1. 40 pp.

USDA 1986 *Crop Yields and Climate Change to the Year 2000* National Defence University Press (2 Vols.)

WALLEN, C. C. 1986 Impact of present century climate fluctuations in the Northern Hemisphere, *Geografiska Annaler*, Series A, 68 A (4) 245-278.

WARRICK R. A., 1988 Carbon dioxide, climate change and agriculture, *Geographical Journal*, 154 (2) 221-233.

WIGLEY T. M. L. & RAPER, S. C. B. 1987 Thermal expansion of sea water associated with global warming, *Nature*, 330 (6144) 127-131

WMO 1989 *The Changing Atmosphere : Implications for Global Security*. Proceedings of the Toronto Conference, 27-30 June, 1988. World Meteorological Organization WMO - No. 710

WORLD RESOURCES INSTITUTE 1989 *The Crucial Decade : the 1990's and the Global Environment* World Resources Institute, Washington 22pp.

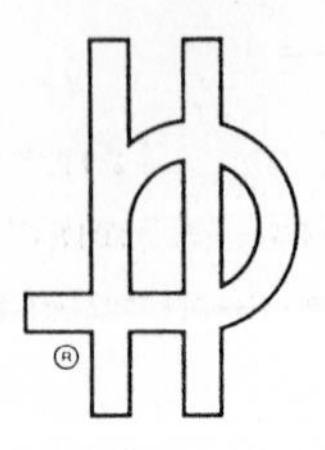

RENDEL ENVIRONMENTAL

Rendel Environmental, the sponsor of this book, coordinates the wide-ranging specialist expertise of individual firms within the Rendel Division of the *High Point plc* group of companies which provides multi-disciplinary consultancy services, on a world-wide basis, for:

- impact assessment studies
- environmental audits
- development of environmental management strategy and policy
- environmental monitoring
- risk assessment

Some 200 specialists in environmental sciences and a variety of associated disciplines comprise the core personnel from whom project teams are assembled. Comprehensive support in all aspects of engineering, economics and socio-economics is available as required from group member firms.

Extensive in-house laboratory and on-site monitoring facilities enable a wide range of environmental parameters to be quantified and assessed. State-of-the-art computer analysis and modelling techniques are used to investigate alternative approaches to complex environmental problems and to identify the optimum solution in each case.

The principal strengths of *Rendel Environmental* lie not only in the extent of environmental expertise available from a single source, but also in the close association between environmental scientists and engineers, which facilitates the formation of imaginative, practicable and cost-effective measures to mitigate adverse environmental impacts.

Contact Dr McL Smith
Rendel Environmental
61 Southwark Street
London SE1 1SA

Tel: 01-928-8999
Fax: 01-928-5566
Telex: 919553 Rendel G